Thomas Sopwith, Surveyor

Thomas Sopwith, Surveyor

An Exercise in Self-Help

Robert Sopwith

The Pentland Press
Edinburgh – Cambridge – Durham – USA

First published in 1994 by
The Pentland Press Ltd
1 Hutton Close
South Church
Bishop Auckland
Durham

British Library
Cataloguing-in-Publication Data

A catalogue record for this book
is available from the British Library

ISBN 1-85821-206-5

Typeset by Carnegie Publishing, 18 Maynard St., Preston
Printed and bound by Antony Rowe Ltd., Chippenham

To Jane and Elizabeth
loving wives
his and mine

Contents

List of Illustrations

Notes on Illustrations

The frontispiece is a drawing by Clement Burlison; 1, 2, 3, 4, 5, 8, 16, 19, 21, 22, 23, 26 and 27 are original sketches or prints from Thomas Sopwith's diaries, notebooks and scrapbooks; 6 is an original sketch by R. C. Sopwith; 7 is from *Treatise on Isometric Drawing*, 10 is from the 1839 Directory of Newcastle and Gateshead (both Newcastle Central Library); 9 is part of an engraving by T. M. Richardson, Snr, looking north, showing the Sopwith showrooms at the corner of Market Street, to the left of the nearer cupola; 11 (Science Museum), 12 (British Transport Commission); 13 is a drawing by T. Wyatt, 14 and 15 unattributed engravings, all three from Sopwith's scrapbook; 17 is possibly from *Illustrated London News*; 18 (Yorkshire Geological Society), 20 (British Geological Survey) are from drawings by Thomas Sopwith; 21 and 25 are both examples of his work held in Newcastle Central Library; 24 is from the bulletin of the International Association of Engineering Geology.

The author wishes to thank the above mentioned sources for permission to reproduce material held or published by them.

Acknowledgements

The inspiration for two exhibitions and this book started in the Sedgwick Museum, Cambridge, although it no longer houses the large model of Dean Forest, and grew in the University Museum, Oxford; the Institute of Geological Science and Geological Museum in London; the Royal Institution of Chartered Surveyors; the Institution of Civil Engineers; the Royal Society and the Hancock Museum, Newcastle-upon-Tyne, the curators and librarians of all of which kindly allowed me access to items. Thanks are due to Robin Gard of the Northumberland County Record Office who drew my attention to the Revd. John Hodgson's journal; to the librarian of the University Library, Newcastle and notably two successive keepers of the special collections and also the trustees of the Trevelyan papers deposited there; to the librarian and staff of the Central Library and of the Literary and Philosophical Society, Newcastle for access to manuscript and printed material. My thanks are due to Alistair Elliot for his advice, to Professor Bill Dearman for generously sharing his knowledge and enthusiasm over geological model-making as well as presenting a copy of *An Account of the Mining Districts of Alston Moor etc.*, and to John Thackray for reading chapter 12. Lastly my thanks are due to Roger and Rachel Hird who gave me such a warm home in Jesmond in which to write.

Preface

"I took him first for an architect, next for a mathematical teacher or professor, but now I think he has to do with the manufacture of steam-engines or some other mechanical art on a large scale". So surmised B. W. Richardson in his personal introduction recorded in the *Life of Thomas Sopwith* published in 1891. Sopwith himself probably preferred C. E., civil engineer, to another self-description, that of mining engineer.

It remains a puzzle how best to describe a man whom his biographer and friend sought to depict in "a modest treatise . . . to include with a brief life of its author, excerpts of some of the incidents which he has recorded". Seeking to present a somewhat more critical view of an albeit able man who achieved much, I have decided to cast myself after all on the mercy of his published works and his diary, a singular document recording his activities. A diary may give a narrow view, devoted to self-advertisement or gossip, revealing doubts or prejudices, very often as a great expurgation of the self. The reader is left to judge; but this meticulous observer did not lack activity of his own and deserves still to be heard as he reveals with enthusiasm and reflection the busyness of his life.

The "self-help" of the title was a concept developed and made famous by Samuel Smiles, who published his book on the subject in 1859. The ability to raise yourself up in society by your own endeavours is a theme sharing something with Napoleon's promotion of careers open to talent and the twentieth century hope for a meritocracy: such a hope has often however been fulfilled with the encouragement of more recognised figures of the establishment or of the social aristocracy. It is perhaps enough to note that Thomas Sopwith was a youth during the post-Napoleonic war period of the Regency and of reactionary politics, but that he rose through the decades of the more liberal Tories of the 1820s, and benefited from both the overwhelming need for reform and the surging age of steam in the 1830s, to reach prominence in the first half of his life. Smiles, who met Sopwith and allowed him to read the manuscript of his *Lives of the Engineers* in 1856, would surely have approved of this further example of self-help. As the son of a freeman of a thriving industrial town, Sopwith did have a foot on a lower rung of the ladder; nor does he fail to remember how much help he received, but a less determined man might have remained a Newcastle cabinet-maker or an unknown mining manager in the Pennines.

Although the enthusiasm of a practical mind did not wane, the year 1845 makes a natural stopping point: he had received the honour of admission to the Royal Society and accepted the post of chief agent of Mr. T. W. Beaumont's lead-mines in Northumberland and Durham. Despite the infrequent reference to his wife and family, it was for their sake he claims to have returned to his beloved Northumberland: however acquaintance with scientists and artists did not cease, nor did travel. A wider world of affairs continued to call forth comment but the year 1845 stands as one of great personal attainment, the height from which he could look with immense satisfaction, and gratitude, upon the course of life taken by a young cabinet-maker and surveyor. He could number among his friends scientists, artists and above all professional men who stamped their skills upon early Victorian England. He was one of them.

Chapter 1

Antecedents and Youth

"I hope you will not forget the advice I have given you and shall always be happy very happy to hear that you persevere in a sober honest and virtuous course of life which are the only properties that constitute a useful member of society and cannot fail of being acceptable both to God and man and that you may be such a one shall be always the earnest prayer of your affectionate Father and Mother. Thos. and Jane Sopwith"[1]

Thomas Sopwith posted this portion of a letter in a scrapbook. It was written not to him but by his grandparents to his father Jacob. A further letter warned against "temptation to wickedness in London". Perhaps Jacob was seeking business in the metropolis or more likely fine woods for his joinery and cabinet-making business. The second letter, dated 14th February 1791 and written from Newcastle went on to advise, "As you have seen and heard of me do and the God of peace shall be with you which is the earnest wish to your affectionate Father and Mother . . . ".[2] A third letter, possibly written when Jacob reached the age of 21 or the end of his apprenticeship to John Watson[3] joiner, which was in 1792, again warned against being led astray "at that period of life in which the temptations to Vice and Immorality is most prevalent".[4] If help was needed to prevent falling from grace, the affectionate father was eager to recommend the son to the grace of God "which (if you are not wanting in your own endeavours) will be able to keep you from falling. We are all in perfect Health but

1

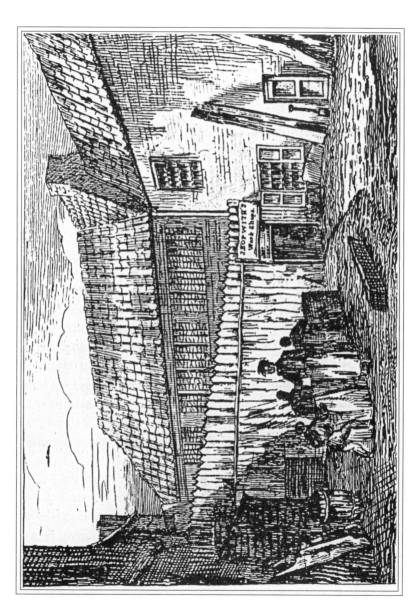

Jacob Sopwith's Yard

has [sic] not any news for you that I can recollect". Grandfather's words had been handed on or left for Thomas to discover. They give a fair balance of trust in God and a call to work diligently which also steered Thomas from the earliest days.

The origins of the name of Sopwith remain obscure. References range from that of Robert de Sokpeth (Soppethe or Soopeth), bishop's receiver-general for Norham in 1311,[5] which is linked inconclusively with Soppit or Sopwith in the parish of Elsdon, to a belief that an inhabitant of Sopworth in Wiltshire found his way north and contracted the latter syllable to a shorter form. An Australian Sopwith descended from master mariners suggests that a Sopworth jumped ship and started anew on Tyneside. But this is all fancy and nor is it clear whether the first Sopwiths to be freemen of Newcastle, Michael Sopwith, Cordwainer recorded in 1685, with his sons Matthew and James, also Cordwainers, were cousins. Speculation ceases with Thomas' careful record in probably his earliest surviving notebook of pen and wash sketches which also includes a family tree.[6]

At the head of the tree is Matthew Sopwith of High Angerton, Hartburn in Northumberland, a farmer. The eldest son was Jacob, baptised at Hartburn in 1709, also a farmer in High Angerton. His son Thomas was born there, "served his time at Morpeth and removed to Newcastle"[7] probably in 1762 where he died fifty-one years later in 1813, aged 72. There is a Thomas Sopwith, Cabinet-maker, in the list of traders in the 1793 directory of Newcastle: this is presumably grandfather Thomas (1741–1813). Jacob, who married first Isabella Pile, daughter of Matthew Lowes, and twice more, had a daughter Mary and a son Thomas, born on January 3rd 1803. We have a sketch of Jacob's mahogany yard drawn and etched by Thomas in 1828. The workshops were probably in Painterheugh, the same that were destroyed by fire in 1833, but Jacob also had an address at 191 Pilgrim Street in 1822.

The choice of schooling for young Thomas is remarkable and

probably providential. If in later days he might have appreciated a modicum of Greek and Latin to hold up his head amongst the gentry and scholars whom he so eagerly sought to know, it was not to be. There were fifty-five day schools in Newcastle and Jacob chose one at 11 Saville Row run by Mr. Henry Atkinson. Thus, although Jacob was in 1823 on a committee to improve the grammar school, which according to the historian Mackenzie had sunk to a roll of only 9 in 1820, he had chosen a school of a very different stamp for his son.*

The mathematical ability of Henry Atkinson was proven. What prevented his appointment as mathematician at the grammar school was his opinions both on religious and political subjects. J. Weir got the job instead. Atkinson's knowledge of square numbers, gravity and the comet of 1811 was intermingled with an "Essay on Truth" (1818) and on the "Effects on different classes of society by an increase or decrease in the price of corn" (1820). It was probably his admiration of Byron's Don Juan which blocked his path to the post at the Royal Free Grammar School in 1823 and also to the Arithmetical mastership at Edinburgh Academy in the following year. But he was undoubtedly an able man and a fine teacher. Thomas Sopwith, writing from Loaning House, Alston in February 1829 believed that Joseph Crawhall, a somewhat pedestrian artist, should be engaged to make a portrait of his late mentor. Atkinson had been set over a school at the age of 13 by his father while a new school was being established. It was not just the ability to set mathematical subjects before the Newcastle Literary and Philosophical Society from 1809 or problems in the Ladies' and Gentlemens' Diaries of 1810 to 1823, but also the practical application of mathematics which won an admiring pupil.

The pupil had ability and serious purpose. A strong desire to write at the age of twelve, a powerful interest in the history and

---

* At some point in his childhood Thomas suffered from scarlet fever. He pays tribute to Bessy Watson who nursed him. She became Mrs Elliott, wife of a Berwick brewer. Diary 2, p. 14.

antiquities of Newcastle and the making of a map at the age of thirteen are the first instances of Thomas' eagerness for self-education.[8] Much later he recalls that Thomas Miles Richardson senior gave him instruction in drawing in 1814 when he was eleven years old.[9] To this Henry Atkinson was able to add encouragement to accurate observation and measurement, the very basis of so much of Thomas' professional skills.

> "It was from my schoolmaster, Mr. Henry Atkinson of this town, that I obtained my first knowledge of the practice as well as the principles of surveying . . . I remember going with him to Elswick-fields . . . acquiring . . . a perfect knowledge of the general principles of surveying . . . Mr. Atkinson was not one of those preceptors who confined his instructions to the school. When he explained the size and distance of planets in the ordinary school lessons, he provided the telescope at his house on clear evenings. The microscope was a means by which he impressed on the minds of his scholars a firm and devout conviction that Almighty goodness and Almighty skill prevail alike in the least as in the greatest of the works of Divine wisdom. It was in this manner that he laid the foundations of deep thought and taught his grateful pupils to feel as well as to know . . . [he] followed up these preliminary lessons by actual surveys, which enabled me not long after, and while yet a pupil in Mr. Atkinson's school, to measure the field in which Higham place in this town is built, for the purpose (and to which the plan I made was applied) of setting out the building-sites of that row of houses".[10]

Fortunately three Georgian houses remain as a memorial in Higham Place. Sadly the vital three large volumes of Sopwith's diary have disappeared since Richardson records, presumably using that source, that Sopwith wrote out, at this early period of his life, "a series of notes on astronomical subjects . . . with descriptions of observations he made from a plain astronomical telescope constructed by himself".[11] There were also notes and catalogues of coins and mineral specimens: his microscope was similarly constructed by his own hands. The methodical approach never left him and although he claims to have had little formal schooling it is clear that he had a good schoolmaster.

Add to his schooling and his own scientific leanings the craftsmanship learned in the joinery works of Jacob and it is evident that Sopwith had all the ingredients for a number of practical careers. He records no other details of his education although he had views on the subject expressed later in his remarks to miners.[12] There is no indication of boyish spirits, athletic activity or mention of his family and home. It is perhaps unlikely that he would have recorded any details of the family scene. His great good fortune lay in his ability to develop his skills without having to be employed in the sort of unappetising work in which inventors or the self-educated so often find themselves trapped before their true vocation emerges. It is nevertheless worth speculating that he might have become an architect even if he would hardly have competed with Oliver, Dobson and Grainger in contemporary Newcastle. The extraordinary fact is that at the age of nineteen he did compete.

The subject of the competition was a design for a new gaol. The choice of design was made by Thomas Oliver and John Dobson under the instruction of the city councillors. That the councillors chose well is clear but it seems somewhat strange that Dobson was in a position to choose his own radical design for the new Carliol square site. He and Oliver were so impressed by Sopwith's design that a second prize of ten guineas was awarded. It was no disgrace to be second to Dobson; and if there was special favour shown to the nephew of the future gaoler, James Sopwith,[13] there is no indication of a manoeuvre on the council. It is stated that father Jacob Sopwith was a builder[14] and there is a brief record of his building work in Newcastle at All Saints church. Later the Sandyford Road workshops and workers' houses were designed by Thomas himself to replace the incinerated workshops at Painterheugh, a scheme well within the compass of an experienced surveyor.

Although no gaol was built to Sopwith's plans the design for it survives. It is recorded by Thomas Sopwith in his *Treatise on*

Isometrical Drawing (2nd edition, 1838) and shows a detailed plan and elevation.* No other designs by Sopwith for a new building showing plans and elevation have come to light. He was involved in designing a covered market for Thirsk[15] but as his diary states he saw little prospect of its acceptance. There are later designs for Richard Grainger which reveal Sopwith's involvement in the improvement of Newcastle and he had views about church design which evidently derived from his interest in the elliptical shape of All Saints Church, Newcastle. He could likewise hobnob with intellectuals on the defective nature of Robert Adams' gothic style in St. George's Chapel, York Place, Edinburgh.[16] Apart from surveying, his draughtsmanship and appreciation of architectural detail found different outlets. He became an illustrator of antiquities.

---

* An interest in places of correction was further aroused by observation in 1828 of the new prisons at Carlisle. The chapel, for its convenience and accoustics, was adjudged superior to Newcastle. The fly-wheel for the treadmill at the Bridewell in Edinburgh was simply dangerous. Curiously it was near the pulpit in the open courtyard and an inadvertent step backward might well be rewarded by a clout on the head proving to be "a passport to eternity" – Diary No. 1, p. 45.

Chapter 2

Antiquarian Illustrator

The young cartographer and local historian who had practised and enjoyed descriptive writing from the age of twelve was drawn into the art of illustration by his own inclination. In 1825 B. W. Richardson relates that Sopwith visited an exhibition of paintings and other works of art held at the gallery in the house of Mr. T. M. Richardson[1] whose works he later commissioned and collected in considerable quantity.[2] He had a keen eye for contemporary events and his native pride in local history brought him in contact with those furthering that cause, notably the Reverend John Hodgson.

The means of introduction to the locally important is not plain. Reference to the generosity of certain early patrons occurs both in his diary and his correspondence,[3] and this debt was recognised again and again. One such was W. C. Trevelyan of Wallington Hall. Whether Walter Calverly Trevelyan introduced him to John Hodgson or not, the Trevelyan interest in the antiquities of the Roman Wall would soon have brought about such a meeting. The earliest sketches by Thomas Sopwith which are preserved show that he was working for Hodgson in the late 1820s.[4] But even before that Sopwith had produced a work of extraordinary competence for a young man engaged on making his living as a mining surveyor. This was not simply a single illustration of a church but a study of the former church and the new building by David Stephenson which is known as All Saints, *A Historical and descriptive account of All Saints' Church, Newcastle* (1826). The dramatic frontispiece gives promise to further views, a promise which is not fulfilled, but the detailed drawing of heraldic arms as

All Saints, Newcastle.

well as the plans of the elliptical building embellish a book which celebrates the old and new churches of All Saints. The new building mercifully survives as an oasis amongst office blocks with at least some clear views of it from across the Tyne and from the East.

The impetus for *A Historical and Descriptive Account of All Saints Church* came in 1824 when the young author was engaged on surveying the plans of the freehold property of the church. The clergy and churchwardens made available statements of rents, legacies, accounts and a list of churchwardens such as he found in the vestry. He even wanted to produce large plans giving the names of the freeholders of the pews, but the impracticability of binding the large fold-out plans led him simply to list these freeholders instead. Artistically Sopwith restricted himself to a fine north-east view of the church; a brilliant rendering of the brass-plate from the tomb of Roger Thornton *c.*1430, both plates being engraved by M. Lambert; the initial letters of the descriptive and historical accounts of the old and new churches; the plans of the new church and five plates of armorial bearings from the tombs of 17th and 18th century men and women of the parish. He probably gained the inspiration for the armorial bearings from a work by Moses A. Richardson on the collection in the parochial chapel of St. Andrews, a work appended to Sopwith's in a well-bound edition. Richardson's work, which has a frontispiece by T.M. Richardson, is dated 1818 and a similar work on the armorial bearings and inscriptions of St. Nicholas was also planned. The church accounts are recorded near the end of the volume.[5]

The accounts of All Saints include several remarkable payments made not only for foxes' heads, badgers' heads and otters' heads but also for pints of sack for new preachers and the more obvious repairs to the fabric. Included in these last is work done by Sopwith's father Jacob in 1816. Jacob had done duty as Church-warden in 1807 and 1808, following in his father's footsteps, for grandfather Thomas was churchwarden in 1798. Holder of pew no. 32 was Henry Atkinson, Sopwith's schoolmaster, and the details of the events and people of the church give a useful record of its life. Such success with pen and pencil encouraged the young author and illustrator to offer his services to others.

The first surviving letter from Thomas Sopwith to the Revd. John Hodgson is dated 28 October 1827: almost the earliest sketches recorded in Sopwith's Memoranda of Views also date from October 1827. This earliest letter is all rush and bustle; a survey completed, a call at Grange Moor, to Meldon, going home by Mitford and Morpeth, at W. C. Trevelyan's and at Mr. Robinson's with a request for the camera lucida to be brought.[6] In January 1829 he is busy etching some plans of Mexican Mines for Mr. Taylor of London. He regrets that he is therefore unable to meet Mr. Hodgson but in ten days time he would be in Newcastle, "when I do not expect that I will have anything to prevent me going to any churches (when?) you want . . . I could meet you at Morpeth or when at Alston will come down to Hexham at any time that you will fix and will have great pleasure indeed in being of any service to you".[7] He was looking forward to seeing the Reverend Anthony Hedley in Newcastle. Here is the busy young man, eager to be helpful but busy nevertheless. A further letter in July reveals a different tone. Hodgson has evidently made some suggestions which are received gratefully. "Dear Sir, I am extremely obliged by the kind interest you take in endeavouring to promote my interests, which is the more grateful to me, that I feel convinced you do so with cordial friendship. I have always esteemed it a happiness to be acquainted with gentlemen whom I so truly respect as Mr. Hedley and yourself, I have regarded your occasional advice to me with much attention and any instance of your kindness and attention is I assure you very gratifying to me." What had Hodgson said? Was Thomas Sopwith humbled by the advice received?

The sketch book,* which gives the vital evidence for these years

---

* This delightful survival shows a variety of sketches, the majority being of antiquarian subjects; some revealing architectural detail. There are also four or five paintings and some notes of a lecture on moral philosophy heard in Edinburgh.

Mitford Church.

shows that Sopwith was engaged in sketching the church at Mitford in outline and in detail in October 1827. Interleaved with drawings of Alston there are a similar outline and details of Morpeth Church. Sketches of St. Cuthbert's, Carlisle, and of Gateshead Park House early in 1828 precede the outline and details of Stannington: there are excursions into Durham at Heworth and drawings of Edlingham church and castle. Several pages have been cut from the notebook and the material on others is recorded as having been sent to Mr. W. Davison, the printer at Alnwick. The pen and wash sketches of Mitford and Morpeth are "drawn for Mr. Hodgson's History." In October 1829 Sopwith writes from his Pilgrim Street offices, chatting about Sir Charles Monck's instructions on the Belsay-Otterburn section of the road and about corporation business, whereas in May 1829 his efforts at sepia wash drawings of Cresswell and Widdrington had ended in his burning the unsatisfactory results.[8] There were further excuses but between 1830 and 1833 Hodgson's letters to Sopwith show that Hodgson had gladly received details of the drawings of Morpeth. In July 1832 Hodgson spoke of his intention to walk "Severus' Wall". In September he wrote that there would be an account of the Roman wall in the next volume of the county history of Northumberland. In June 1833 Hodgson wrote to congratulate Sopwith on Telford's invitation to him to be a member of the Institute of Civil Engineers and later in the same month thanked Sopwith for his new publication on the mining districts of Alston. In July a great digging was to start at Housesteads and Hodgson wanted sketches of the wall.

How did Hodgson evaluate Sopwith's work of illustration? Public acknowledgement is made in the introduction of the History of Northumberland Part 2 Volume 2, "and to the zeal and kindness of Mr. Sopwith, surveyor, I am indebted for correct delineations or engravings of various churches, chapels, and other subjects" as expressed in the list of plates. Here on the title page was Morpeth church; Woodhorn church, Newbiggin and Widdrington chapels, Stannington church, Morpeth gateway, Cresswell tower and fossil tree, Ulgham chapel and Roger Thornton's tomb were all included. It was a good contribution from a young professional surveyor seeking business and preferment, who had also produced his own topographical work. Hodgson thought he was seeking more.

An inkling of Hodgson's coolness towards Sopwith's zeal is suggested by a letter written to the illustrator apropos of one in which Sopwith had recorded the generosity of Mr. Surtees, historian of Durham. "I am glad to hear of Surtees' liberality," wrote Hodgson, "but it is his character, which is not only noble but kingly in its way. From me you must expect little more than thanks, which, though they have little feeding in them, I must contrive to make as savoury as I can the next time I step before the public in the character of county history cook." This he had clearly done in the introduction of Part 2 volume 2, but Sopwith wanted more. Hodgson committed to his journal his full scorn and irritation for a zealous young friend who expected too much. The passage is worth quoting in full: Hodgson's journal entries are not usually so elaborate.

"31 July 1832 – Wrote to Mr. Sopwith and hope he will cease to torment me with endeavours to extort a greater extent of praise from me than I can consciously give him. He has been found [and cursing? – the words are crossed out and illegible] sparing [sic] with me ever since I wrote my preface to part II volume II in which he thought me perhaps too sparing of commendation for the services he rendered me in sketching: but I would not say in the preface that I esteemed him as a friend and entertained high notions of his talent, so that he might say to his children how intimate Mr. Hodgson was with your father and what a high opinion he had of him. This he in letters expressed a wish I should do. But there is still so much selfishness, vulgarity self-opinion and unbounded vanity about him that I shrink from making any such declaration: though I do indeed highly value his services without [entering? – indistinct] any minute of the use I have been to him in recommending him to profitable and popular jobs besides by reasoning with him and introducing him to good company greatly cured him of a [illegible] and most ignorant opinion he had of the private habits and the requirements of families of rank – amongst whom none could be more greedy of being introduced – or more condescending, though none of them had the tythe of his conceitedness or his vanity. As yet he is an impudent thorough-paced worldling, avaricious and bursting with the love of glory – one whom no praise could satisfy – though he pretends to be all humility and full of religion."[12]

No letters have been unearthed which explain this outburst but it pinpoints the problem. Sopwith expected not just thanks but praise. That praise could then be used to advertise to others the regard in which a scholar and historian held him and Hodgson resented being so used.* It is gratifying to know that Sopwith not only later was prepared to take on Hodgson's son in a professional capacity[13] but was offering "to copy altars at Ryton",[14] hoping to be at the wall in the spring of 1833[15] sketching at Housestead Crags, Craiglough Crag and altars in July and offering his services "with the chain or a pencil in 1834". Drawings of Whitley station on the wall or churches were offered, general busyness noted, and further hope of being at Hartburn or Haltwhistle in 1836 expressed. Then disaster struck. A Mr. Sly had lost drawings of the wall. Nevertheless, Sopwith had a plan of the wall for a few miles from Henshaw to Chesterwood. Would that be of use? Perhaps Hodgson would have been happier to receive fewer enthusiastic assurances in favour of a quieter life. In 1838 Hodgson states that if he had "five heads and ten hands" he could not complete the work before the meeting of the British Association in August of that year. In the event, there are only two illustrations by Sopwith in Hodgson's history vol II part iii: neither was of the wall, but one was indeed of Whitley or Whitelaw Castle, also known as Castle Nook, near Alston.

The historian of Durham, Robert Surtees, also used some of

---

* The same practice may have been attempted in Sopwith's pursuit of John Wilson, Professor of Moral Philosophy at Edinburgh, from the lecture room to his home. Professor Wilson's breezy style made him well able to handle his visitor.

Sopwith's drawings. One such was a drawing of Gainsford Hall, another was of Ancroft church. A rather different subject was that of St. Anthony and Pigs, to which Surtees refers in a letter of 5 June, 1831. Surtees also doubted Sopwith's wisdom in the latter's search for important introductions, but on the other hand used Sopwith's influence to find a place for a former servant in a Newcastle inn.[17]

The practical observer in Thomas Sopwith undoubtedly enjoyed the work of illustrator. It was a compulsive habit, often practised at first light, to go out and sketch a church, the tracery of its lights or details of stonework on the tower: later he would encourage and commission artists such as T. M. Richardson senior and J. W. Carmichael, for whose 1839 engravings of Fountains Abbey Sopwith provided written descriptions. Likewise ancient Roman inscriptions or artefacts were obvious subjects to record and their recording an opportunity to rub shoulders with the gentry at Wallington Hall and Capheaton House, the Trevelyans and the Swinburnes. Perhaps Sopwith had jumped a little too high too quickly but he retained an interest in sketching antiquities and buildings throughout his life as a practising surveyor.

Chapter 3

Northumbrian Surveyor

The work of surveying then as now covers a large number of skills. Today the profession is split up into specialisations which divide quite sharply the skills of physical delineation of existing features and the estimation of the value of resources when managed and developed. Thomas Sopwith knew no such divisions and left his mark on all aspects of the profession with equal success.

The early education which he had received made him ideally suited for his chosen profession. His ability as accurate recorder of detail which he had trained his eye to see through telescope or microscope, and his critical appreciation of land and its measurement led his enquiring mind to look further. Henry Atkinson, his schoolmaster and teacher, had given practical applications from his own mathematical mind and passed on insights to his pupil. Not least he may have recommended Sopwith's help in the survey of Higham Place, Newcastle. There is something highly satisfying in drawing up accurate representations by means of plans and Sopwith's work in this field shows a fine degree of competence.

To further his competence he made use of isometric projection. A consideration of isometrical projection occurs in a later chapter.* He was not original in this, and if one critic complained that he wrote as if he had invented it, Sopwith took care to use the skills of Mr. Peter Nicholson, an architect and geometry author, as well as critical excerpts by Professor Farish, who probably did largely invent it, and J.C. Loudon, the garden designer-architect, in

---

* Chapter 14

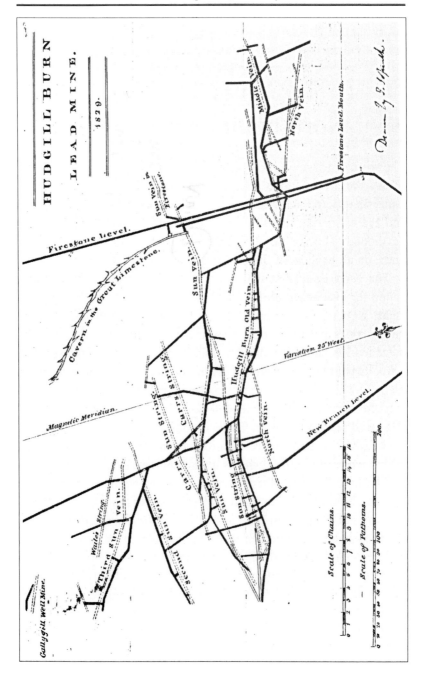

promoting his treatise.[1] These were indeed names which would give standing locally and nationally. Later Sopwith was instrumental in raising a subscription for Mr. Nicholson who had fallen on hard times. Loudon he often met and in the year 1843, after Loudon's death, wrote in his journal a full appreciation of this self-taught botanist and author.[2] At this stage their names added lustre: his treatise, not surprisingly, gave examples of work in which Sopwith had been involved. After a general commendation to miners, gardeners, builders, engineers and botanists, especially to ladies amongst amateur artists, the author expanded on the reasons for keeping mining records. Mr. Taylor, superintendent of Alston Moor for the Greenwich Hospital mines, and Mr. John Buddle, the distinguished Wallsend colliery viewer, in his paper delivered to the Natural History Society of Northumberland, Durham and Newcastle upon Tyne, both emphasised the value of keeping mining records, a subject always held dear by Sopwith. Here too were names already useful to him. He argued in the treatise that it was well worth buying plans like those he had done for Holyfield and Hudgill lead veins. Mining partners ought to afford an engraving at ten shillings and sixpence with further plans at five shillings. Likewise the partners at Holyfield ought to afford £5 p.a. on a mine with profits of £5,000 p.a.

To persuade people to use mining plans was one aspect of enlarging efficiency: the possibility of a survey covering a region would provide other means. His treatise on Isometrical projection included a plea for a correct geological map of the northern counties of England as part of a "statistical map of England" which would be of use to the Tithe Commutation and Poor Law Commissioners. Sopwith had already been drawn into the work of administration on behalf of the government in 1833: doubtless he saw the possibilities of more work and more approbation at the highest level. What sort of circulation did his writings have? At a time when the Ordnance Survey was greatly extending its interests, the plea did not go unheard and Sopwith's own contribution in surveying the Forest of Dean may be seen as serving one part of government reforms: involvement with modern education at the new University of Durham, indirectly a result of Whig pressures upon the last prince-bishop, Van Mildert may be reckoned another.[*]

In 1837 there were "Observations on Surveying, Planting and Computing the Area of Extensive Districts, with Reference to Surveys for the Commutations of Tithes, and to the Practicability and Advantages of a Natural Survey". A copy of this appears in the catalogue for the sale of Sopwith's books in 1879. It was undoubtedly a response to likely work emerging from the government's decision to commute the tithe to a money payment charged on land to pay for churches and their clergy. Particularly disliked by those who dissented from the Church of England, commutation did little to commend itself to society at large. What was meant by a "Natural Survey"? It certainly meant work for surveyors and the publication consisted of 24 large plans, but whether it was used in the profession widely or not, no evidence has emerged.

The artist in Sopwith lead the author's readers from the usefulness of mining plans and regional geological survey to consider the architectural uses of isometric projection. Here was the Revd. Anthony Hedley's Chesterholme and Sir John Swinburne's Capheaton, rebuilt in 1668 by Robert Trollop, architect of the Old Exchange, Newcastle. Sopwith remembered Trollop in another context: when the stranger's pocket guide to Newcastle was "hastily written" for the 1838 British Association meetings, he could not resist including Robert Trollop's epitaph at Gateshead.

> Here lies Robert Trollop
> who made yon stones roll up
> when death took his soul up
> His body filled this hole up.

---

[*]   See p. 26 for a direct encounter with Bishop Van Mildert.

Sopwith enjoyed curiosities and humour behind his serious purpose of enlightening the public. His naïvety has an engaging quality[3] noted by the historian Surtees even if his methods did provoke others to wrath. There was certainly one other who was angered by him, but that was in the course of doing his duty, not pressing personal interests. Of that, more later.

As any economist knows there must be a market for the produce in existence or that market must be speedily created if the processes of production are to remain economic. Sopwith's own reflections upon the usefulness of a railway are early enough in the history of locomotive transport to be questioning both proposed speeds and the expense of maintenance unless the towns linked by rail were large. These thoughts were provoked by travelling on the Liverpool to Manchester line in 1834.[4*]

Graphic description and valuation were thus allied in the young surveyor. Apart from one list written in pencil indicating a building contract such as any quantity or building surveyor would recognise, there are few details in known correspondence which bear Sopwith's hand. His own assessment of the importance of the early transport surveys is summarised in his diary.[5] The design for the Otterburn Road from Newcastle was an especial pride, a task which resulted from an introduction by the Revd. John Hodgson to Sir Charles Swinburne. The second major routeway was the new Derwent road which brought him in contact with Mr. Surtees of Hamsterley Hall. Although he published in 1838 *Observations on a proposed road from Shotley Bridge to Middleton in Teesdale: forming a turnpike road from Newcastle to Liverpool*, he was probably most pleased with the Otterburn road. He won the contract in competition with Mr. John McAdam.

The Otterburn road had been partially surveyed by McAdam in 1828 but the route or manner of survey had been questioned. Sopwith stepped in to make the survey in 1829 and in 1830 was

* See Chapter 7.

up in London to hear the proving of the plans and evidence in both Houses of Parliament. Although the references to the Otterburn road survey are infrequent, it is possible to imagine energetic activity and progress, both walking the line from Belsay to Whelpington and Otterburn[6] and back in the office in 23 The Arcade, Newcastle. Here, he states, "my arcade office works well. 2 to 2½ hours at the workshop before breakfast. At the Arcade at 9 a.m. till 9 or 10 at night – plans, sections, Drawings, Etchings, Ledgers, Time books, furniture designs – never at a loss for occupation or variety".[7] There were hold-ups. He comments that Sir Charles Monck "has hardly behaved well to me".[8] A letter of apology for absence records the need to go and bury his father.[9] The Parliamentary survey was due to be completed by November 30th 1829 and the lengths of the road "in the several lands through which it passes"[10] were set out in detail that autumn. An estimate, probably by Sopwith, for 18 miles between Newham Edge and Otterburn gives measurements of 21 feet wide to a depth of 9 inches. Preparing a bed, the winning and breaking of stone, cartage and construction of conduits would come to £11,001 16s. 6d., without including fences and bridges. He warned that 9 inches depth would not be enough: another 5 inches and properly broken would prevent larger stones working to the top. Sir Charles Monck was restive but his choler was principally directed at the laziness of the surveyor Luke Pearson.[11] In February 1830 Mr. Ellis, Monck's agent, was "so ill that he could not discuss the proposed new road".[12] The road was in use by early 1833 however and stands as a fittingly executed contract from the time of the original appointment by the surveying committee of the Corporation of Newcastle.[13]

A final contemporary appreciation for the Otterburn Road appeared under the initials of V. W. (Vicar of Whelpington), namely the Revd. John Hodgson, in the *Newcastle Courant*.[14] Bearing in mind Hodgson's frustrations at the lack of time Sopwith could spend on drawings of Roman and other antiquities, his praise is generous:

Bishop Van Mildert.

"The view of this new line will be a matter of rejoicing and the most
agreeable surprise. The levels along it are beautifully preserved,
and, though its line is slightly serpentine, it is exceedingly direct.
It sweeps, as Mr Sopwith, its surveyor, in his report to its first
promoters well observed, through 'a succession of hollows admira-
bly adapted to make it easy and picturesque.' "

Hodgson could not forbear adding that he hoped that adjacent
parishes would be encouraged to do some road work to keep up
this fine carriage-way.

The new Derwent road leaves the Scotswood and Hexham roads
at Axwell Park Gate and takes a route by Winlaton Mill, Lintz Mill
and Ebchester to Shotley Bridge. Its great merit was one of
improved gradient. As the notes attached to the plan of the "Vale
of Derwent New Road" tell us, the old road went by way of
Windmill Hill, Marley (Marlow) Hill, Burnop Field and Medom-
sley to Shotley Bridge. "The very steep and inconvenient ascents
and descents of this line" were shown on a sketch of the comparative levels. The plan[15] survives but no other information has yet
been uncovered, although the venture is also likely to have been
promoted by the corporation of Newcastle. The road was built.

One early railway survey brought Sopwith into contact with a
great dignitary and with such disappointing impressions that he
devoted more than three pages of his diary to comment on the
occasion. Bishop van Mildert, the last prince-bishop of Durham,
was perhaps facing the deprivations of Whig and Tory reforms in
general. He assented at once to the young surveyor's request that
the railway should pass through his lands between Blaydon and
Hebburn but when Sopwith tried to show him the plans, his
lordship pushed them away from him. The young surveyor felt he
had been treated most rudely and harshly and left "with feelings of
perfect astonishment and regret that a shepherd could set so poor
an example to one of the humblest of his flock".[16]

Despite the unfortunate brush with the bishop of Durham Sopwith continued with local surveys on behalf of the gentry both

before and after his work in the Forest of Dean. These included a Proposed Improvement of the River Pont near Stamfordham bridge (1836) on the subject of which there were several letters to the land agent Mr. Sample: the interests of both Sir Edward Blackett and Sir John Swinburne were involved. There was work on behalf of the Great North of England Railway which led to viewing Mr. Thomas Cookson's estate at Hermitage,[17] and Blackett manors were surveyed at Ridley, Thorngrafton, Henshaw, Melkridge and Westwaters. There were parliamentary committees for the Newcastle Gas and Waterworks company and the Durham Junction Railway between 1834 and 1836. Drawings were made of the proposed railway between Blaydon and Wylam, part of the Newcastle – Carlisle railway, the construction of which he viewed after travelling by coach to Hexham in July 1833. In August 1837, the expert eye of Dr William Smith, "father of geology", was cast on proceedings when he joined with Sopwith further along the line.[18]

The great flurry of work presented by tithe commutation, the now successful development of locomotive power on railways and the consequent competition from road companies gave any surveyor more than enough to do. Others engaged in similar tasks would suffer ill-health, probably more from the wearisome nature of giving parliamentary evidence than from frequent travel. Sopwith himself was ill with rheumatism from March to June 1835, yet the immense activity served only to spur him on to seek means of improving the efficiency of his operations. To this end the craftsman in wood served the surveyor and man of affairs.

Chapter 4

Craftsman in Wood

The Incorporated Company of Free Joiners of Newcastle-upon-Tyne separated from the Carpenters in 1589. In the late seventeenth century veneering and inlaying developed which led to the admission of foreigners, not originally permitted when neither Scot nor alien could be apprenticed. The 1778 directory lists 33 Master Joiners of whom 16 were members of the Joiners Company, including Farringtons, Sopwiths, Robsons, Liddells, Renwicks and Jameses. Grandfather Thomas, apprenticed at Morpeth before coming to Newcastle in 1762, and father Jacob, established the cabinet-making and joinery business in Painterheugh in 1769 and in Pilgrim Street. Uncle James Sopwith was also a joiner and builder at Dog Bank.

The joiner and cabinet-maker's craft required accurately fitted structures and familiarity with fine hardwoods. This skill and knowledge Thomas Sopwith brought to bear on three particular projects which were of direct use to him and which he also persuaded others to use. These projects produced the improved levelling-stave (1833), the monocleid desk (1838) and geological models (1839 and later versions). All went into production and examples of each can be found today. A rather more sketchy evidence of other Sopwith furniture exists and it may be that much remains to be rediscovered. It is possible that he was not a significant designer of furniture but rather left popular patterns to be produced by his cousin John.

The land surveyor's equipment, along with the chain, pencil and notebook such as young Thomas had used as a schoolboy in

Higham Place, requires the inclusion of an accurate means of measuring levels. A theodolite and staff were both in use, the latter requiring a considerable height for using on steep gradients. Various versions were available to Sopwith. In 1853 a small textbook* of surveying and levelling for schools shows in its frontispiece Gravatt's, Sopwith's and Barlow's levelling staves, copied from a plate in the *Encyclopædia Metropolitana*. The little instruction manual by T. Sopwith F.R.S., F.G.S. was "reprinted chiefly with a view to Gratuitous Distribution by the Author to Mechanics' Institutes and Libraries in Union with the Society of Arts". Others might have it for sixpence or by post for one shilling from Mr. J. Tennant, 149 Strand, London. The illustration of Sopwith's stave in this later manual which sets down his paper of 1848 addressed to schoolmasters of Northumberland, Durham and Newcastle-upon-Tyne complements an earlier work. In the preface he states that "the existence and progress of all knowledge consists

1. IN ACCURACY OF OBSERVATION

2. IN FAITHFULNESS OF RECORDING

3. IN FACILITY OF COMMUNICATION TO OTHERS"[2]

In the same manual Sopwith praised the value of the good education he had received from his schoolmaster and the whole pamphlet reflects something of his views on education continuing throughout life. But it was twenty years earlier that he had put his mind to finding a good levelling-stave and had decided to construct his own.

The impetus for this decision probably came from the need for quicker operations of surveying and also from the intention to produce a more accurate instrument. Road surveying might not need accurate levelling but recent years had seen the increase of its practice, and for railways, sections were absolutely necessary. For drainage in agriculture and "for many purposes connected with

---

* Practical Observations on Surveying and Levelling.

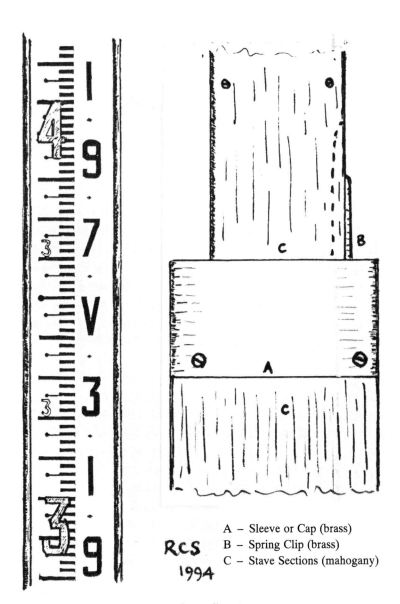

A – Sleeve or Cap (brass)
B – Spring Clip (brass)
C – Stave Sections (mahogany)

RcS
1994

Improved Levelling Stave.

geology and mining, exact levels of the surface of districts are often required."[3] Accuracy over several miles overland and underground to a matter of inches was vital for aqueducts. Errors might cause, and had caused, great and needless expenditure and Sopwith's avowed aims in his first little instruction on the subject were to shorten the time and increase the accuracy: that was the object of his Improved Levelling Stave. Existing staves had one to three rods with a scale in 12ths or 10ths of a foot, a cross vane to slide and an aperture through which the scale could be read. An assistant responded to signals from the observer, moving the vane up and down and reading the scale which was usually checked by the observer. Dependence on a possibly careless assistant, the manoeuvres required using back-sight and fore-sight staves and the difficulties of moving a vane in line with the cross-hairline in a telescope all delayed the practice of surveying. The rods responded differently in wet or hot weather and most of the levelling staves in existence were simply unreliable in action because of inferior materials and construction. One such was W. Gravatt's Stave, described in detail in F. W. Simms *Treatise on the Principal Mathematical Instruments* 4th Edition 1838 and in Sopwith's own *Practical Observations on Surveying and Levelling.* A. Nesbit's *Treatise on Practical Land – Surveying* 5th edition 1833 also deplored the lack of a serious treatise on levelling.

The great advantage of the new stave was that, "the surveyor reads for himself at the very moment of taking the observation."[4] No vane was required because the surveyor would look through his telescope at a broad and clear graduated scale of the levelling stave. The telescopic rods would be fully extended and held in place by spring-clips between the first and second, second and third sections of the stave. The rods would slide loosely within each other and there would be no screw with potential damage to the rods. The holder of the stave, the surveyor's assistant, could now concentrate on holding the stave upright.

"Mahogany is the best wood that can be used in the construction of levelling-staves," he writes.[5] How fortunate for Sopwith that he had the means to lay hands on a good supply of the wood and the skills available to work the material. He goes on to state that "plain or strait-baited wood, as workmen call it, should be selected, and it ought to be well-seasoned". The surface should be saturated with linseed oil, stand for a few days and have a final covering of French polish to render it impervious to the weather. So in these few words we have the practising surveyor setting out the principle which the joiners in his workshop would grasp: better still, we have an illustration of the stave in the workshop where it was constructed. The levelling-stave was the most widely-used of Sopwith's creations. In 1836 he records in his diary that Mr. Simms had ordered one hundred of them and it would be fair to say that well over a hundred years later surveyors could be found who referred to their "Sopwith" or "staff" before the expense and weight of mahogany caused the staff to be superseded. Such an apparently humble instrument is not mentioned in B. W. Richardson's biography, but it seems likely that Sopwith equipped his assistants with the new stave as the party resumed the important surveying work in the Forest of Dean on December 16th 1833. Cousin John Sopwith and the work force at Painterheugh and later at Sandyford road would be busy meeting Mr. Simms' order alongside their more usual cabinets, tables and chairs.

A more original creation by the cabinet-maker was itself a cabinet, the celebrated monocleid. The first versions of this were invented in 1830, according to Richardson. The busy man of affairs had already experienced the need for orderly arrangement of his papers and the answer to the problem was a large cabinet doing the duty of a bureau with a big capacity for storage, namely a substantial filing cabinet. Such a cabinet was certainly available in 1832 when Sopwith describes the planning stages in his diary.[6] The name was suggested by his highly-esteemed friend the geologist Dr. Buckland[7] and the description of the cabinet which needed only a single key to release doors and drawers was prepared in time for

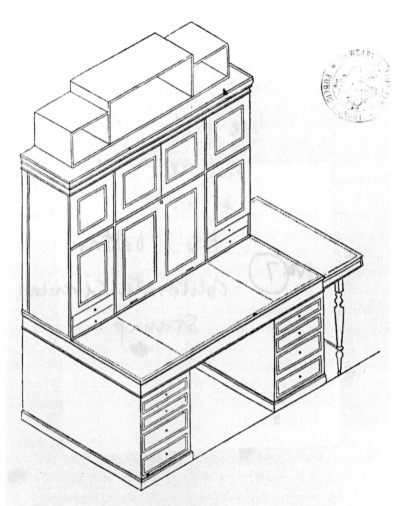

THERE are few persons engaged in official business, in professional pursuits, or in extensive correspondence, who have
not experienced much inconvenience from having to keep
their various papers, books of frequent reference, &c., in
different drawers, closets, or boxes, each requiring a separate
key: the loss of time and the difficulty of...

Monocleid Desk.

the eighth meeting of the British Association for the Advancement of Science held in Newcastle in August 1838.

"Adapted to save much time, and to secure a systematic arrangement of a great number and variety of papers", the monocleid was described in a short pamphlet.[8] It is drawn in isometric projection and shows a large knee-hole desk with an apparently over-heavy superstructure. Approximately five feet wide, the table top or desk part is about two feet deep enabling quite large plans to be studied. The superstructure is four feet high, discounting an open bookshelf above. A large flap hinged at the base lets down in the centre, and is covered with leather, green-cloth or oil cloth to form a writing desk. The edges are rebated to overlap rebates on all adjoining doors and drawers. The superstructure or upper cabinet is only some twelve inches deep but has a large number of drawers, closets and partitions. All these will be automatically locked when the desk-flap is secured by the single lock in the centre of the bureau. Thus a great many pigeon-holes and drawers are readily accessible to a person sitting at the desk: each space was appropriate to the contemporary sizes of ledgers, letter-books, cash-book, diaries or other books of reference. There were drawers for sealing-wax, wafers and stamps, for drawing materials, colours and hair-pencils. There were grooved slides for holding pens, pencils etc. and spaces below for inkstands, scales and snuffers and tray. The writer could have within his reach "whatever is of frequent requirement in reading, writing, folding and sealing letters, parcels etc . . . .". It was all to save time.

A free-standing version without a top is also depicted with as many cubby-holes under the sliding side-pieces. But the really remarkable feature was the linking mechanism between the upper and the lower part of the cabinet-cum-desk version.[16] "To the back part of each drawer an iron plate is affixed, and, by means of a very strong and simple adjustment of iron-work, each drawer is liberated the moment the door (or flap) is opened". Thus it was unnecessary to have separate locks on the desk drawers: each was freed or secured as soon as the central lock was turned by the single key. Sopwith was very proud of the system.

In his pamphlet the cabinet-maker states that the invention is by Thomas Sopwith C.E., manufactured and sold by John Sopwith, Grey Street, Newcastle-on-Tyne. It would cost between £20 and £50 according to materials, dimensions and number of divisions within. Alexander Milne of the Commission of Woods and Forests used one and doubtless other patrons would follow. In the 1840 polytechnic exhibition in Newcastle the catalogue included a monocleid, but the catalogue of 1848 did not do so. In 1842 Mr. Body of London had a black walnut monocleid with looking-glass panels, gilt borders and Louis X1V style carving. It cost £95. In 1851 a heavily-ornamented neo-baroque version was shown at the Great Exhibition which was the occasion of winning a medal by T. and J. Sopwith. This medal appeared on the bill-heading in the late 1880s at the time of supplying bird-cases to the new Hancock museum. Recently no less than three examples of a monocleid existed in the possession of the late Earl of Harrowby who had used one in his study for most of his long life. A further piece of one had until recently a less honourable place in the stable of a house belonging to another Sopwith engineer and surveyor! The assurances of convenience were not unfounded but the weight of the monocleid and the conclusive nature of security or liberation by the single key militated against usefulness by jamming. It was nothing if not ingenious and a travelling writing-table or desk with removable legs and without the cabinet top was also constructed on the same principle. This latter was able to fit into a compact box 22 inches long, 18 inches wide and only 5 or 6 inches deep, the legs being stowed within or carried separately.

The third project which Sopwith followed through in his workshops has the nature of a work of art although its purpose was entirely practical. In the 1848 catalogue of the polytechnic exhibition referred to above there were simply examples of woods used in the cabinet-making business, no furniture; but in another room were series of geological models constructed from these woods. The long experience of geological strata and topographical knowledge were combined to be expressed in what were designed to be teaching aids for students, a series of solid wooden models of geological form that remain both pleasing to the eye and to the hand. It is however more appropriate to refer to them in a subsequent chapter. Although there is little direct evidence of Thomas Sopwith's furniture designs remaining, the geological models alone should demonstrate to all his craftsmanship in wood: the staff and the monocleid were delights of design in their time. The latter won recognition in the Great Exhibition itself and must surely have set the Sopwith furniture showrooms buzzing in Grey Street, carrying on the name of a solid family business established over half a century earlier.

Chapter 5

Topographer and Landscape Romantic

The rôle of author was one which Thomas Sopwith had no difficulty in assuming. A list of his works might appear to make this claim inflated: descriptive pamphlets of now forgotten instruments, techniques and furniture together with observations addressed to miners, schoolmasters, fellow geologists and meteorologists. The style is often didactic, frequently unexceptional and perhaps by reason of the subject matter, even mundane. It is however practical and exudes all the confidence of a man who knows that what he has to say might be as useful to others as it was to him. So it is that he not only published a work of architectural interest and competence at the age of 23, namely *The Descriptive Account of All Saints' Church, Newcastle,* but he also wrote a work of topographical interest which captures the atmosphere of the bare uplands near Alston as well as that of the dales of Wear and Tees. This format was repeated in his later *Notes on Egypt* and *A Month in Switzerland* and combined his usual practical observation with titbits of information about events and places.

The particular interest of *An Account of the Mining Districts of Alston Moor, Weardale and Teesdale,* where he combines descriptions of scenery, antiquities and geology, is that the descriptive sketches he gives are by written word rather than by drawing. There are only three simple if dramatic drawings of natural features, one of a geological feature and one of a Roman altar. Ale Burn Cavern, Cauldron Snout and High Force are depicted with far less authority than that of which Sopwith was capable. He is happier with the geological feature and the Roman altar at Whitley fort or Castle Nook. Perhaps he lacked confidence at this stage in his career or found the scale of pinching together a small page-heading, rather than showing a larger sketch illustrating the geo-logical form of a prospect, restricting and difficult. Reproductions of the sketches, whether etched by himself or not, would be expensive. We know that he was sending off sketches to William Davison the printer at Alnwick, but they were mostly of houses and churches for a history which Davison did not ultimately produce. The sketches were printed separately, engraved by J. Kerr. Several of the preliminary drawings appear in a notebook in which sketches for Hodgson and the occasional landscape occur.[1] Much larger pencil and wash sketches were made, perhaps at a later date, but whatever the reason Sopwith presented the results to Davison his "much esteemed friend, the printer and publisher, who with more of admiration of the country it describes, than any prospect of pecuniary recompense, offers it to the public in its present shape". Thus was launched the author's main topographical work.

The content of the *Account of the Mining District of Alston Moor etc.* is based on three routes out of Alston, the heart of the area which Sopwith had come to know so well as assistant to Mr. Joseph Dickinson, agent for the Greenwich Hospital Mines in the region. The journey starts at Hexham after an introduction pointing out the overall physical features of mountain and dale as well as the climate and the condition of the roads. The route from Hexham passes the new Chain-bridge at West-Boat, Warden which he sketched, during its construction, in 1825.[2] Details of length, of the four pairs of chains, the "deflection of Catenary" and of the cost of nearly £5,000 are given. The ensuing details of the Free School and Almshouses founded by the Revd. John Shaftoe also refer to the value of the estate as well as the restrictions laid upon the Schoolmaster and teachers as to residence and salary.

Where then is the romantic author in all these descriptive details?

High Force.

T.S.

"The vicinity of Hexham is extremely beautiful, and the views from the neighbouring eminences are fraught with variety and interest". He reflected, and invited others so to do upon the "wide, smooth and placid surface" of the Tyne especially at evening when it had "much of the sublime effect of lake scenery". Likewise leaving Haydon Bridge, "the route to Alston intersects a narrow and romantic valley, through which the road winds in a circuitous course; a wall of rocks on one side and a very steep and high woody bank on the other, with a small stream between, have a romantic and secluded effect more often found in the deep and lone recesses of forest scenery than immediately adjoining a turnpike".[3] This style is mirrored in the writer's diary for with his observant eye he delighted to record the landscape as he walked or rode through it. The journey continued through Whitfield rising up to Whitfield Fell with a view of the West Allen and to the east the great hills of North-East Northumberland, even to the sea in clear weather. Over to the Pennines, Crossfell "gradually unfolds its gigantic summit". The South Tyne, which is depicted from Newshield in Sopwith's *Memorandum of Views,* is observed with pleasure, the scattered white-washed houses on the lower slopes imparting "some liveliness to a scene in which wildness and sterility much prevail".

It is good that *An Account of the Mining District of Alston Moor etc.* has been re-issued: it is full of descriptive detail such as he had practised writing from his boyhood and expresses all his interests. Subsequent chapters on Alston Moor dwell much on the history of Alston while the geological phenomena and waterfalls predominate in the Tynehead, Nentforce Level section. The Nentforce level itself could be navigated by boats 30 feet long and the impressions of excitement are delightfully portrayed – the lights, the mineral veins, the dress of the adventurers and their songs of companionship as they enter the hillside. Chapter 4 brings out the detailed knowledge of the Roman fort at Whitley which he had studied and on which we had reported to Hodgson, W.C. Trevelyan, and others. An outline of a shoe size sent to Miss Emma Trevelyan's collection appears on a page of his Memorandum[4]. The high ground of Crossfell is the subject of Chapter 5, followed by accounts of Hartside, the the Helm wind and the caverns of Ale Burn and Hudgill Burn. Chapters 8 to 10 deal with Geology, the strata of Mining Districts and Mineral Veins before he describes the old and new methods of working lead mines in a long chapter which is subdivided into accounts of Teesdale and Weardale. Here there are not only illustrations but occasional verse, including Mrs Heman's "The Homes of England".

Sopwith himself wrote some lines on Alston Moor[5] and there is a certain wistfulness attached to Alston Churchyard where his first wife Mary Dickinson was buried soon after the birth of their only child, a son, Jacob. There are several little views both of the church yard itself and looking out past the end of the church[6] but perhaps Sopwith wisely refrains from putting the verse he composed in to the text of his topographical work. Nevertheless he combines practical comment, an appreciation of the beautiful landscape and a plug for his newly-surveyed road in the vale of Derwent in the final pages of his account. So he moves from "the yawning aspect of the rocks, torn asunder by repeated torrents" to reflection on the "subterranean treasures almost unexampled in the annals of mining" in Hudgill Burn and to observing that a new road is about to be made along the banks of the river. It cannot be denied that he writes with an authority based on firsthand experience and, despite his comments on the Alpine climate, commends a relatively unexplored and remote area where the "genuine worth and hospitable kindness" of the "excellent inhabitants of the mining districts will be found one of the chief attractions" by those who visit "the hitherto neglected portion of the Kingdom".

The later publications already mentioned, *Notes on Egypt* and *A Month in Switzerland*, occur after the year 1845 when Sopwith had traversed a great deal of the uplands of the United Kingdom before returning to his native Northumberland. Although there is relatively little mention of Allenheads in *An Account of the Mining*

Districts of Alston Moor etc., he was to make his mark in Allendale from 1846, giving full rein to his interests in the efficient organisation of mining operations and in the education of its inhabitants. The busy schedule which he set himself travelling on mining and surveying business rarely excluded an opportunity to walk, ride or drive with the eye of a keen observer upon the landscape about him. Three occasions when he had less pressing business and more time to appreciate his surroundings were on a visit to Ireland (October–November 1838), to North Wales (October 1841) and to Yorkshire (September 1842).[7]

The visit to Ireland was very much a business trip for he heard in only mid-October of 1838 a request to make a mineral survey in the West of Ireland which began in November. He received useful information from the geologist Sir Richard John Griffiths F.R.S. about the area of Ennis which was to be visited. Sopwith summarised in *General Notes on My First Visit to Ireland* first travelling and secondly scenery: he further discoursed on buildings, institutions, religious services and ceremonies, hospitality, national character and finally "Religion and Present Condition and Prospects of Ireland". After seeing the Bay of Dublin and Phoenix Park within the City, he drove through Tipperary where delay was occasioned by an insensible form in the middle of the road. The body proved to be alive but intoxicated. It was rainy through Limerick but near Ennis he enjoyed the variety of the well-wooded parts in contrast to the bare limestone rocks of the Burrin mountains. "These are truly sublime and of the highest interest in a geological point of view" and which were likely to yield rich mineral deposits. "The views at Burrin, the shores of Galway Bay, the mountains of Connemara, the bold, bleak and rocky promontory of Blackhead ('O'ill luck to it,' says Paddy, our post-boy; 'may it be a long day before I see its ugly face again') and the coast of the Atlantic were all fraught with deep interest". The Shannon viewed from Cahircon and the beautiful lake and hills of Scarriff caught his imagination and he would have liked to have written at greater length of the "succession of interesting, sublime or beautiful scenes which in summer must be still more delightful". He moves on instead to the architectural grandeur of the public buildings in Dublin as well as to the "most melancholy sights connected with the subject of Irish buildings . . . I was prepared to witness much misery; but imagination, however fertile, will never picture the sad and horrible and gloomy aspect of these dwellings of the Irish poor".[8] Like many other visitors to Ireland he was staggered by the squalid poverty of the worst hovels.

The visit to North Wales with Dr. William Buckland, the celebrated geologist, began from Chester on October 11th 1841. Armed with Greenough's geological map and Ordnance Survey maps the pair went first to Ellesmere to examine the different meres before passing the aqueduct or "Pont Cysyllty", which Sopwith described, being a fitting construction by Thomas Telford in the valley of Llangollen "the picturesque scenery of which is justly considered as one of the greatest attractions in North Wales".[9] "The heavy rain spoiled the journey a little and he seems to have preferred the richness and grandeur of the Vale of Clwyd. He and Buckland were looking for signs of glaciation and they paused, again in heavy rain, at a new cutting on the road near Corwen. The churchyard of Corwen was reputed by some tourists "as being the most romantic in Wales".[10] Certainly it caused Sopwith, rising at 5.30 a.m. next day, to sketch the view from the entrance, "a woody eminence of great height and steepness – the dark and lofty brow presents in several places the bassetting of the slate rocks . . . a waterfall descending gives great interest to the landscape". Walking over rough tracks to Pentre Voilas, he was reminded of the wilds of Alston Moors and felt that the landscape hardly compared with the luxuriant beauties of Llangollen or the rugged grandeur of Snowdonia. The Swallow Falls were well up to expectations after such heavy rain as the travellers had continued to face: Nant Francon, the Menai Bridge, Llanberis pass, Aber-glaslyn and Drws-y-Coed were equally magnificent.

The visit to Yorkshire, also in Dr. Buckland's company, was for the purpose of a meeting at Wakefield of the West Riding of Yorkshire Geological and Polytechnic Society. After the meeting Sopwith and Buckland with a Mr. Howson and Mr. Jackson made an expedition to Clapham Cave, near Settle. "It would require a large volume and a vast number of drawings, to convey any tolerable idea of the beauty of this place . . . here a stately column, there a noble dome, a clear lake reflecting beautiful groups of pendent (sic) stalactites, the water flowing in curious pulsations over round masses of rock, some places reminding one of the modelled ruins of an ancient city, and others presenting a facsimile of Alpine glaciers". One rock was dragon-like: some of the stalactites produced musical tones. "It is a marvellous, transcendently beautiful, a deeply interesting and instructive lesson of Nature's silent but effective labours even in the bosom of the mighty hills, where unseen, unknown, unthought of, this cavern has from age to age been forming, and is now for the first time presented to the wondering eye of man". A storm only four years previously had opened up the cave. "On our return we examined some scratched and polished rocks by the side of the lake, one of which Dr. Buckland suggested should be preserved by having a cover over it". If the last statement somewhat reduces the power of the previous passage, it is a reminder again that the man of science notices the practical suggestion of preserving geological as well as mining records.

The practical observer in Sopwith often stopped short of a description by simply falling back on the word "interesting". This was frequently the case in his description of conversations too where the reader of his diary is tantalised to know on what subject the interesting discourse might have been. As a romantic however there was one occasion of pure farce which resulted from his determination to meet for a second time the hero of romantic prose, Sir Walter Scott.

In his very first surviving small Note-Book or Journal, adopted for its convenient pocket size in place of the three ledger-sized books, the substance of which were circulated amongst a few friends, Sopwith has a pen and wash sketch of Abbotsford – drawn in passing, April 24th 1828. He had set out from Carlisle to Hawick on April 3rd, following the Esk and sketching Gilnockie Tower from the gig. Beyond Langholm he enjoyed a wonderful drive viewing lofty mountains "but what added most interest to the scene was the circumstances of meeting in these romantic solitudes the most eminent Man of his Country, Sir Walter Scott, whose writings have so much increased the interest and associations of the localities noticed in them . . . and whom, even to have *seen* is an occurrence worthy of remembrance especially as on this occasion it had the associations of being the first day of my being in Scotland and in a situation so peculiarly romantic [no punctuation] he was in his travelling carriage accompanied by his daughter – it is pretty generally known that this admirable and fascinating writer is not remarkable for any external indications of genius – a dull and rather heavy expression of countenance is indeed wonderfully brightened up by the vivacity of his social spirit . . . but his is not in its general aspect the poet's eye that Shakespeare has so loftily conceived and so beautifully described – his manners are universally described as extremely engaging and his disposition – open, – candid and generous – his courteous behaviour and great hospitality as well known, but it is said have latterly had some restriction forced upon them by their tendency to induce his admirers to seek the charm and interest of his society – and who the rank and numbers of these are considered extending from the 'Throne to the Cottage' ".[11] This was not the end of the writer's delighted encomium upon the poet, historian, antiquary and novelist whom he was so pleased to have seen. He reflected not only on Scott's "fertile and luxuriant mind" as being far more enchanting in its outpourings than that of the average historian and topographer, but also upon the author of Waverley's contribution to the "union of National feeling" and the benefit for Scotland conferred "by the Numerous Tourists of Rank who visit the Scenery consecrated by his Muse".

Did he speak to Sir Walter Scott? It appears not. Where on the ranking order between throne and cottage did Sopwith place himself? How ready was he to respect the great man's privacy or press his own claims to visit him? The answer is to be found in the correspondence of Robert Surtees, historian of Durham, transcribed by James Raine.[12] As with Hodgson, so with Surtees, Sopwith was determined to use the influence of an author to enlarge his acquaintance with what he called great men. Surtees sent a plenary introduction to Sir Walter Scott enclosed with his letter of Jan. 29th 1831. Thomas Sopwith was setting out on his honeymoon with his second wife Jane Scott. Surtees hoped that Sopwith would not disturb Sir Walter Scott in Edinburgh where time was short but that he might find "the noble Lion in his den" at Abbotsford. A snowstorm however intervened. What was Sopwith to do? If he could not meet the great man, he could not waste the letter of introduction. Perhaps he should send a present. He contented himself with sending the letter of introduction with a piece of Bride Cake! Surtees meanwhile hoped Sopwith would help in the application and humbler introduction of Surtees' servant to a post as publican at the Black Horse in Pilgrim Street, Newcastle. He enjoined Sopwith to continue his diary and "may the stream flow as clear and pure to the end".[14]

Sadly the wedding cake appears not to have been acknowledged, nor the letter. Surtees said that he dare not write a second letter of introduction to Sir Walter Scott but that Scott "forgets nothing – Lord forgive him for his memory – but if you are near Melrose – and I am sure your delicacy will create the right road to it – if you find Sir Walter is well and send up your card with any little reminiscence or a wish to take a likeness of the Enchanter's Den he will recollect your name. Further just now I cannot do".

It seems unlikely that Sopwith ever saw or met Sir Walter Scott a second time. In his second diary he records a story told him by Mr. Kyle while on the crags above Smallholm. Walter Scott's lameness as a boy was so troublesome to his nurse that she thought of throwing him over the scars and actually went out for that purpose, "but remorse of conscience prevented this romantic and premature mode of disposing of the Border Minstrel and if correct, strikingly exhibits the influence which very feeble instruments may sometimes be permitted or restrained from exerting in the destinies of the world".[15] Delicacy or no, this particular hoped-for introduction to Scott seems not to have born fruit. Doubtless the romantic strain was in retrospect satisfied by the first sighting of the great man.

Admiration of the Waverley Novelist did not require total agreement on the question of ivy-covered ruins, a sine qua non of the romantic writing of the Gothick age. Scott had suggested to the Duke of Northumberland that repairs should be made to Hulne Abbey.* In consequence ivy had been removed and the walls pointed with Roman cement giving the appearance of a badly-built barn instead of venerable ruins. "Ivy, though sometimes destructive, is a great ornament," stated Sopwith, and he was not surprised to hear that tearing it from the walls of Hulne Abbey had greatly impaired the appearance and beauty of the building.[16]

Such a romantic approach to life in the wilds in young adulthood was cheerfully enough derived from the young admirer's enjoyment of evening on Alston Moor

> In Evening Shades the eager soul
> Bursts the dark fetters of controul
> And all its contemplations rise
> From this dull earth to vaulted skies .[17]

It would be many years before he had the leisure fully to pursue the secrets of the vaulted skies in the practical sciences of astronomy and meteorology. For the moment eagerness and contemplation joined in happy union, simply expressed and exultingly enjoyed.

---

* The popular name for Hulne Priory

Chapter 6

Newcastle Improvement

The immense changes of the first industrial revolution were bound to affect a city with such a leading part to play in industrialisation as Newcastle. The production of coal, its shipment and overland transport from the pithead gave impetus to life on Tyneside. Iron smelting to provide cast iron for railways, lead and glass-works were amongst the heavy industries practised. With the raw materials and ready fuel supply, the age of machinery had every hope of flourishing in Newcastle. As Samuel Smiles quotes in his *Lives of the Engineers*, Newcastle was "the Eye of the North and the Hearth that warmeth the South parts of this kingdom with fire".

Fuel became the staple produce of the Tyne region and its transport presented some difficulties in the steep streets, wynds and chares of the old town. From panniers and pack-horses to road or tramways involved the use of planks, flag-stones and plate-ways as at first strips of metal were nailed to the planking and then cast-iron plate-ways were fastened to wooden sleepers. Such ways led out on to staithes on the river bank, if below the town, and coal could be tipped straight into ships. Above the old bridge of Newcastle however the coal had to be transported in the shallow-draught keels with their square sails and rudder-oars. The movement of more coal led to a demand for improved means of transport. The careers of George and Robert Stephenson are synonymous with the early railway age as steam locomotion replaced horse-drawn traffic. That of Thomas Sopwith was certain to find work as a surveyor of new lines of railroad as well as new carriageways fit for mail coaches for increased passenger and business needs.

The wealth generated by coal soon found its expression in fine buildings, both residential and commercial. The Newcastle of industry was also that of commerce. Architects and builders competed to build a city worthy of the increasing activity of its citizens: Thomas Oliver and John Dobson aided by Peter Nicholson and Richard Grainger, respectively theorist and entrepreneur, became the motivating forces, eyed shrewdly by the town clerk John Clayton, which forwarded this purpose of building a fine, Georgian city with magnificent markets and wide streets as the mediaeval town finally burst out beyond the tight-knit intricacies upon the banks of the Tyne. Thomas Sopwith was a surveyor, exercising that skill of rapid measurement and valuation of properties so important in planning the expansion of any growing community. If he was more of an observer than a politician or active entrepreneur, he nevertheless was an apologist of the new spirit of expansion, eager to promote the schemes of Richard Grainger.

Whether or not the first contributions by the young surveyor are regarded as improvements in that process which altered the face of Newcastle, there is no doubt that Sopwith was excited by the possibilities and played his own small part. As a schoolboy he was surveying in the area known as Higham Place, parallel with the street commemorating John Dobson by name, tucked now under the lee of the Laing Art Gallery. At the age of nineteen he had designed a gaol for the site in Carliol Square which was not accepted and his later support for the idea of bringing court and lock-up closer together was also unsuccessful. In the exercise of his professional work he had extended his architectural and other interests by commemorating All Saints' Church, old and new, in his descriptive and historical account.

The amount of encouragement which Sopwith received is difficult to gauge. All schemes promoting change have their opponents and this is evident if only by implication rather than direct evidence.

Old established businesses would be anxious concerning the planning of new buildings, new streets and new undertakings of water-supply, road-making and paving. Was the expense merited? Were the advantages illusory? And would not some gain at the expense of others? Sopwith stood for office as Councillor for the West Ward of All Saints but appears to have been unsuccessful. His handbill issued on December 28th 1835 from the Royal Arcade gives due thanks to those Electors who did vote for him and to those friends who did not because they thought that his professional work would either suffer or take primacy. He assured the Electors that he was willing to hold office if thought suitable, that he had abstained "from asking even a single Vote" and finally hoped that the "unremitting Exertions" of those selected would be "directed to promote the Improvement of the Town, and the Welfare of its Inhabitants".

What then had he done? Outside Newcastle he had been involved in both the Otterburn road and new Derwent road as well as the Blaydon and Hebburn railway, surveying for the owners of the land and the directors of the companies concerned. His work for Newcastle was much more sketchily recorded, the evidence complicated by the additions he made to his diaries later in the 1830s. This much is clear from his diary: he was occupied in London attending the Parliamentary Committee for the Newcastle Gas and Water Works Company on April 21st 1834 and on April 29th John Buddle was examined on the Durham Junction Railway "on which I was also in attendance at the Committee". This was followed by further attendance on a House of Commons Committee on March 27th 1835 after a painful journey because of rheumatism, and attendance on a House of Lords Committee at which he was allowed to be seated, still suffering from rheumatics. Surveys of the Great North of England Railway were pursued in November and December 1835. To return to 1830 it seems likely that his first parliamentary business had to do with Newcastle. He attended a Committee of the House of Commons in the Smoking

Room and present were Sir M.W. Ridley and Mr. Ord, as well as Mr. Ellison, Mr. Liddell, Mr. Bell and Mr. R.J. Wilson. The Committee adjourned because of a petition from the Free Burgesses of Newcastle respecting the Town Moor. Perhaps this refers to an early attempt to put a railway across the Town Moor which was later under discussion and is illustrated by Sopwith's drawing of the "Proposed Arrangement for Concentrating the termini of the several Railways near Newcastle upon Tyne", dated 1836. It is more likely to refer to encroachments or alterations at the Southern end of the moor or in the Leazes. A further suggestion could be that the Great North Road was being improved.

The fullest evidence of Sopwith's involvement in the heart of Georgian Newcastle as surveyor and draughtsman for Grainger's plans is displayed in an isometrical plan of the improvement of Newcastle dated June 11th 1834. Three days later the *Newcastle Journal* carried an article entitled "Proposed Improvements in Newcastle" which bears the stamp of Sopwith's views. A copy appears in the Reminiscences.[2] Excitement akin to a strongly contested election had been aroused but "the merits of the case are so obvious to all who regard it with an impartial eye that it is a matter of surprise and regret that any portion of the respectable inhabitants of the town could be found opposed to it ". There were in fact over 5000 in favour and only some 300 against. "To Mr. Grainger's talents, perseverance and capability of executing this great improvement" even opponents' testimony had been given. The writer goes on to identify the new street extending from Dean Street to Blackett Street, stating that it would exceed Regent Street in London in width. It was to be 80 feet wide: polished stone buildings along it instead of mere painted stucco would further show its superiority to London. There would be fine shops and the public benefit of "four hundred thousand pounds circulated through the town in wages and other disbursements". A new era had begun. "Who would have supposed ten or twelve years ago that such buildings as Eldon Square, Leazes Terrace and the Royal Arcade could have been so speedily and successfully executed by one individual". The article praises the patronage of the Corporation, lauding its wise capital expenditure which would stimulate trade and commerce.

The best clues in the newspaper article of June 1834 which point to Sopwith's hand are its praise of the Newcastle-Carlisle railway, the Durham Junction railway and "the Derwent, Otterburn and other new roads". All of these enterprises had occupied him and he was obviously proud of them. Nevertheless there was an opportunity to pour scorn on the opposition: a hairdresser, "afraid to compete with a few streets", had published an advertisement against the plan and "excited the ridicule of every reasonable person". The butchers would be far better accommodated in the new covered market with its eight new entrances: there was no doubt of the great excellence and public advantage of the project. The mere three hundred opponents could be forgotten.

The linking of riverside Newcastle with the upper town had always presented some difficulties because of the steepness of the ascent from the Quayside. Thomas Oliver's plan had recently been published when Sopwith set out his own promotion for the improvement of Pilgrim Street where he had premises at number 191. An abstract of his report appears in the Newcastle Journal of October 21st 1837. It was read to "a meeting of gentlemen friendly to the improvement of Pilgrim-Street".[3] Pilgrim Street had been the principal thoroughfare and was suffering from the increased traffic engendered by Newcastle's growth. "From the Ouse Burn on the East to Skinner Burn on the West there is only one thoroughfare that is conveniently passable for carriages from the lower to the central and higher parts of the town, viz the Side and Dean-street which are steep and irregular in ascent and circuitous in direction; part of Dean-street rises at the rate of 1 in 9½ but the proposed new street would be a uniform rise of only 1 in 13½, would be very spacious, and perfectly straight in direction from the east end of Mosley-street to the Quayside with a branch street to the Sandhill".

Grey Street, Newcastle.

The project was explained, the expenditure and probable return on the investment detailed: the calculations were based on Thomas Oliver's plan produced during Sopwith's absence in London. This could be improved by widening some streets but Sopwith professed to have no feeling of rivalry towards other plans. A convenient street from the centre of the town to the Quayside "would be highly important because the termini of the Newcastle and Carlisle, the Great North of England and the North Shields Railway, were all fixed at the central level of the town" with consequent increased traffic to the Quayside. From Pilgrim Street to the Quay there would be a saving of 530 feet and even from the foot of Grey Street a saving of 280 feet. He had taken great care "to arrive at a proper estimate of the purchase of property, and its value, when the street was completed". The builders Mr. Grey and Mr. Brown had examined and expressed entire approval of the valuations and estimates. It was not to be.

Earlier in 1837 Sopwith had the pleasure of a visit from Dr William Smith, the "father of English geology", whom he introduced to Richard Grainger. They walked to see Mr. Grainger's new buildings and Sopwith commented on the "easy manners and leisure of one who might be taken for an unconcerned spectator rather than the prime mover and mastermind of the most gigantic and truly splendid enterprise". Grainger showed them plans and elevations of the streets currently being built, mostly drawn or directed by Mr. R Wardle in Grainger's office. They discoursed on the nature of various flagstones from Gateshead, Arbroath and Caithness before going to Sopwith's office, meeting en route Sir Edward Blackett and later his agent Mr. Sample. Sample joined in looking at the plans of various Blackett manors and Sopwith's diary then "lists the other plans now in progress in my office":

1. A Plan of the North Banks of the Tyne from Scotswood to the Spital on a working scale of 2 chains to an inch for the Newcastle and Carlisle Railway Company.

2. A Plan and detailed Sections of that part of Elswick Estate which

adjoins the River Tyne and which is intended to be laid out as Sites for Manufacturers and streets etc. by Mr. Grainger who also proposes to erect a new quay of considerable length.

3.   A Plan and Sections of a projected extension of Pilgrim Street to the Quayside and Sandhill, this improvement is included in the New Act for the improvement of the Town passed this last session of parliament and is highly desirable both as affording a convenient access" etc.

The plan put forth in similar fashion in October, a defence of Pilgrim Street "which must otherwise be deteriorated by the superior attractions of Grey Street".

The Grainger improvements had stirred up opposition throughout 1837. Dobson's plans for the Corn Market (1814), the continuation of Blackett Street (1820), the opening of the Nunnery grounds for a public market, thirty foot wide streets and a mansion house and finally the redevelopment of the area south-east of St. Nicholas church had all been rejected.[5] Grainger on the other hand, the speculative builder and man of means, had erected Blackett Street, Eldon Square (1826–32) and Leazes Terrace (1826): he was not so easily put off, Sopwith seconding pro-Grainger plans at two parish meetings in October 1837[6] but nevertheless Grainger found the struggles of the decade continuing and the arguments rumbled on.

The reverberations had not quite died down when *The Stranger's Pocket Guide to Newcastle-upon-Tyne and its environs* appeared in 1838. Sopwith apologised that it was hastily written but it was prepared in time for the visitors "expected at the Scientific Meeting in August 1838". The occasion was of some importance to Sopwith and he would duly enjoy the meeting of great scientists at this eighth meeting of the British Association for the Advancement of Science, as well as advertising the part he had played and was still playing in the practical applications of science in Newcastle, the north of England and indeed in the fields of mining and geology across the land. He reminded his readers of Mr. Grainger's munificence but feared that the detailed plans for building the courts, council chamber and corporation offices between Market Street and Hood Street would be determined "by local interests and prejudice" rather than by "considerations of intrinsic merit". The guide referred to Grainger's development of Greyfriars gardens, the Royal Arcade with "the offices of Mr. Buddle, Mr. Sopwith and various other professional gentlemen" – he mentioned Peter Nicholson and Donkin and Stable – and finally set out the true extent of Grainger's recent activity. The whole of Grey Street, Market Street, Clayton Street, Grainger Street, Nun Street, Nelson Street, Hood Street and Shakespeare Street, together with the Theatre, Butcher markets, Green Market, Central Exchange, Old and New Music Halls and the new Dispensary had been transformed or created in four years.

The pocket guide was a reflection of all that interested him or displayed the part played by Sopwith in the recent history of his town and region. Here again was reference to the Derwent and Otterburn roads, his praise of Grey Street, grander than Regent Street or Edinburgh. The Roman Wall and the Newcastle-Carlisle railway were not forgotten and nor were other railways, to North Shields, the Brandling junction line and the railway to York. If the author was proud of the achievements in his town it was with some justification.

It may be instructive to notice what parts of the town were shown to an important visitor in 1837. Despite considerable inconvenience on the day before Sopwith was due to visit London to give evidence on the London and Brighton railway, the Earl of Durham's agent, Mr. Morton of Lambton, begged him to help show the Count St. Aldegonde, a Russian nobleman, some of the sights. Mr. Morton explained that St. Aldegonde was a general in the Russian Service, a friend of the Czar and most interested in scientific research. In a three hour tour of the town St. Aldegonde was shown, at his own request, iron and glass works, steam locomotive manufacture and Pattison's lead refinery. Not one to lose a good opportunity, Sopwith showed the visitor plans and sections in his own office as well as "the Isometrical plan in Mr. Buddle's office", presumably

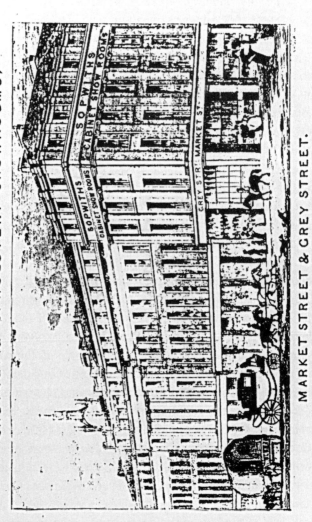

T & J Sopwith Showrooms.

the plan showing Grainger's intended improvements, before walking to view Grainger's new market. Back at the office copies of
some of the plans for new streets were given and models admired.
The Czar, who had visited Newcastle in December 1816, had
himself seen many of the principal manufactories and would have
descended a pit at Wallsend with Mr. Buddle but apparently had
demurred at the last minute. The Literary and Philosophical Society were next on the list for St. Aldegonde: here he saw the Law
and Medical Libraries, the Lecture and apparatus rooms, the general library, reading and committee rooms, the natural history
museum, geological and antiquarian rooms and the gallery of
Roman altars. He saw Buddle's sections of coal strata and the
model of coal workings with Buddle's ventilation system. St.
Aldegonde was at last taken to Hawthorn's where William Hawthorn showed him the locomotive works. Sopwith meanwhile
dispatched George Shadforth to show the visitor Cookson's glass
works, but still pursued the matter of mineral surveys and in
relation to South Russia before bidding him goodbye.

There were two other matters in which he was more directly
concerned and with some success: a report for the Health of Towns
Commission and the building of a grand new workshop, yards and
workers' cottages. The Commission to report on the Health of
Towns in Newcastle heard Dr Reid's report at some time in
mid-decade, which led to sub-committees being set up: the geological structure and level drainings sub-committee consisted of
Sopwith, Robert Nicholson, Dobson, Wallace, Brooks and Wardle.
There was a nuisance and cleansing sub-committee, especially
considering slaughter-houses; a supply of water sub-committee,
looking into baths and washing-houses for the poor and a third
committee was for fire prevention and consideration of accidents
by fire. Sopwith sat on the second and third, not unmindful of the
destruction by fire of his Painterheugh workshop in 1833. A street
widening sub-committee would look at old and new buildings,
several local parsons were represented on the State of Mortality

with regard to local circumstances sub-committee and public walks also had separate recognition. Dr Reid hoped that spaces or parks and walks for the exercise and recreation of the poor would not be forgotten.[8]

Sopwith chaired the Geological, Sewerage and Drainage sub-committee and delivered its report. The burns running into the Tyne were shown on a diagram, only the Lort Burn being arched over in a drain as yet. The natural drainage lines were favourable but the clays, both yellow and blue, in the soil and sub-soil were an impediment to good drainage, causing damp basements in dwellings. Water-drainage pipes would be suitable for the lower, steeper parts of the town whereas vehicles for the "frequent removal of manure at proper hours" would be needed in the central and upper parts of Newcastle. No new buildings should be set up without paved or macadamised roads and a record of all public and private drains should be publicly available. Flood liability was occasional and slight and the only obstruction to natural drainage in the Tyne itself was the bridge with its numerous piers. The sub-committee had used Thomas Oliver's maps as the most accurate plan of the town in the absence of a public survey *per se*. Life in Side and Pandon Dean was impaired by increasing sewerage problems although the Corporation had provided reasonable service over the years. Drains from private houses were not yet regulated until the point at which they reached the streets and public sewers. The main sewers were described in detail with the cost of their cleaning: street, court and alley cleansing were also noted. The report was moved to be received and the motion carried unanimously.

The great force behind public health politically was Edwin Chadwick. Chadwick visited Sopwith at the Museum of Practical Geology, London, at a later date, discussing the health of towns, doubtless hearing Sopwith's views on sewerage and drainage. If the health of whole streets and towns was uppermost in the surveyor's mind at this time, so too was housing for the poor and for his own skilled workforce in the cabinet-making business.

Barras bridge over the Ouseburn was on the edge of Newcastle in the 1830s. In 1839 T. & J. Sopwith Cabinet-makers and furnishers who traded in the town until 1935, took a 99-year lease on an acre site on the north side of Sandyford Road as it leaves Barras Bridge. Here the new workshop, timberyard and workmen's cottages were established, completed in 1838. In 1844 the *Penny Magazine* of the Society for Diffusion of Useful Knowledge had a supplement devoted to the manufactories of Newcastle. The new workshops featured in it and to go with the article Sopwith commissioned J. Storey to depict the main cabinet workshop or manufactory. The author of the *Penny Magazine* article described the buildings, some 300 feet in length in total: the main workshop was 200 feet long with polishing room and joiners' shops and the mahogany shed was situated beyond. At right angles were drying-rooms, upholstery rooms, and the office and storeroom neatly arranged at the angle with foremen's houses at the end of the shorter arm and other workmen's houses on Sandyford Road itself. The scene in the workshop is illustrative of Thomas' particular inventions; the huge monocleid to the left, of the pattern which would later be exhibited at the Great Exhibition of 1851 and win a medal, the Sopwith staff to the right, and on the second bench, part of a model of the Forest of Dean and the smaller geological models which were sold in sets to students or presented to learned institutions. Two of the figures in the workshop are identified as the two long-serving foremen George Muras and Ralph Renwick who had worked for Jacob, Thomas and John for 48 and 49 years respectively. But the most relevant feature in the context of improvement, shown in plan on the illustration and described in the article, is the provision of workmen's houses.

The houses were commended for having almost every room with "two sides contiguous to the open air". They were either two or four room houses, each cluster of four houses being served by two entrances and a shared yard, giving greater freedom of air than four small yards. The yard was flagged and had "a pump, a dust-pit,

coal-houses and other out offices", presumably privies, "all removed from the houses themselves". The rooms could be both
living and sleeping rooms, lest the occupants could not afford
separate ones, equipped with range, oven and boiler. This avoided
heat-wasting fire-places. There were reservations about the cook-
ing efficiency of current English stoves, but the general arrangement was admired in the light of Chadwick's 1840 Report on the
Sanitary Condition of Towns and the subsequent Health of Towns
Commission still at work.

The part Sopwith played in the improvement of Newcastle is
difficult to assess. As an expert professional witness before the
Houses of Parliament his competence cannot be denied. A good
proponent rather than debater, his spoken and written reports were
valuable, both in their own right and as part of the armoury which
Grainger needed to carry out his plans. Sopwith was probably
impatient but also persuasive. His energies on behalf of Newcastle,
its history and institutions, its thriving commercial and artistic life,
were a major part of his life in the 1830s. Nevertheless, his zest
for travel carried him much further afield and with increasing
realisation of the value of communications, he was setting out by
coach and train to his own great advantage.

Chapter 7

Traveller by Coach and Train

The spirit of enthusiasm with which Thomas Sopwith strode the moors and dales was equally evident in other modes of travel. As a young man he records excitedly his first visits to London by coach. He became acquainted early with the Liverpool to Manchester railway line, partook of the unsatisfactory arrangements for the opening of the Newcastle to Carlisle railway and noted the decreasing length of time required, or greater distances covered, as the railway network was extended in his life time. Later he would experience travel on the European continent and with Robert Stephenson in Egypt but those journeys form no part of the first forty years of his life in which short ferry trips by water may be seen as natural adjuncts to his overland travel in the British Isles. Always the observant eye took in the topography of the landscape through which he travelled.

It was travelling that altered his habit of keeping a diary. The earliest record had been kept in large, ledger-sized books but pocket-sized books had been used for notes certainly since April 1828 when he visited Scotland. His first surviving recorded travel in Note Book or Journal No. 1 was a ride in a gig for 6 or 7 miles along the valley of the South Tyne with Mr. William Davison of Alnwick and Miss Davison. The road beyond Hartleyburn was bad and they "trotted along in a somewhat uncomfortable manner" but were soon so amazed at the huge workings for the incipient Carlisle railway that their minds were "in some measure 'diverted' from the badness of the roads and the desolate character of the surrounding landscape".[1] The jolting did not deter Sopwith from sketching

Lambley church as they made for Brampton. Not surprisingly he comments on the great Military Road to Carlisle in contrast, "wide, level and in excellent condition".

The next stage of his journey, from Carlisle to Hawick, was 44 miles. He arose at 5.30 a.m. and started at 6 a.m. It was a fine, clear but chilly April morning. The first road was good, the turnpike wide and the countryside towards Longtown well cultivated. The geology and landscape is described and breakfast was taken at Longtown. The sturdy gig took the route along the Esk, sometimes winding close to the burn, sometimes through plantations. A small runner passing by a drain under the road is noticed and at 40 or 50 yards on each side of this is a toll gate. Tolls were paid at each gate: the gig had crossed the boundary into Scotland. He noticed the border reevers' strongholds, reflecting on more peaceful times as he rode and sketched "Gilnockie Tower, once the stronghold of Johnnie Armstrong who was killed with 40 of his followers near Linhope".[2]

The most exciting part of the trip for Sopwith was meeting Sir Walter Scott in the midst of the landscape.[*] The journey continued to Moss Paul Inn and on through less interesting country to Hawick where the party arrived as the curfew bell rang at 8 p.m. They stayed in the Tower Inn, conversing after supper with the landlady, Mrs Kell, until 11 p.m. after which the diary was written until nearly midnight. He was fortunate then, and usually, in sleeping well and enjoyed an early morning walk in the town before leaving his friends and catching the "Sir Walter Scott" coach at 10 a.m. He did not believe that the hilly route to Selkirk, 12 miles away, could be covered in 50 minutes. However a competitor about a mile behind them spurred the coach-driver "at a pretty rapid rate, the proverbial ambition of the race of Jehu's being further stimulated by the opposition".[3] He does not state at what time they reached Edinburgh but he drank tea at Steventons, by the Black Bull Inn in

---

[*]   See ch. 5 above.

Leith Street, before walking in the city. Although he had asked to be called at 4.30 a.m. for the return journey he had only finished packing at 1 a.m. Consequently he snoozed off and then looked in alarm at his watch which said half past five. "The coach left, at the other end of the town precisely at ¼ before 6 and with the utmost exertion of dexterity I was just enabled to hurry on my clothes – fasten my portmanteau – take a draught of ale, and some bread in my pocket, run as fast as I could along Princes Street and gain the coach in which I was to depart from Edinburgh just at the moment it was about to leave".[4] It is not clear how far he had to sprint but like many travellers he was reluctant to leave kind friends and an affable landlord.

A more methodical account of travel appears in his description of the first visit to London in 1830. In the same diary appears the expenses and total time taken on three journeys on March 7th, March 17th and March 22nd, the shortest time being 30½ hours on the return from London to Newcastle. The details appear to have been appended later and Richardson, who also quoted Sopwith at length on his first journey to London, states that the surveyor liked to compare the facilities and economies of travel in the 1870s with the conditions of these earlier days. He loved the coach and four but hoped that the turnpikes would see busier days again with a steam or electric engine in due course.

The notes describing the earlier stages of the journey remark with admiration upon the beauties of Durham's castle battlements, the Wear with its woody banks, the Prebend's bridge and the splendid towers of the cathedral. The county's roads were less commendable. Yorkshire's were better and so were the views to the east from Thirsk. There was snow left on the hills. A number of neat mile-stones of wood or cast iron with raised letters and numbers of metal marked the way. The minster at York was known to him by the study of Halfpenny's book on the subject but he could not gain entrance on this occasion. He slept much of the way, glad to be inside from the cold, as far as Doncaster. Breakfast was taken at Stamford after which the general flatness of the landscape with its many windmills was noted. Huntingdon's new gaol had a lofty stone wall which he thought was unwisely strengthened by numerous narrow buttresses. Almost any sailor could have scaled them. Not long after, the journey began to change character as a new driver took over for the last 60 miles.* At the end of the long haul southward he could boast "After taking a cup of tea I felt not the slightest fatigue from the Journey". So claimed Sopwith after 38 hours on the move.

Travelling was such a pleasure to him that he rarely found it irksome. If not observing the view he frequently struck up a conversation with other travellers and sometimes encountered "great names", seizing the opportunity to make himself known to them and satisfy his appetite for further knowledge or skills. One such great name was Mrs Somerville. He encountered an elderly stout gentleman, a lady and a young gentleman in the Edinburgh Mail which left London at 8 p.m. However it was not until next day at Grantham that he noticed the luggage of Dr Somerville and the name Mary by which the elderly gentleman addressed his daughter, causing Sopwith to think that the daughter bore a striking resemblance to a bust at Chantrey's.[6] Conversation about scientific people and events confirmed his suspicions and he was delighted to meet the authoress of *The Mechanism of the Heavens, Connection of the Physical Sciences* and other works. Sopwith's comments about Mary Somerville's self-education and yet domestic femininity might not be acceptable to many today but follow the line of approval which Samuel Smiles himself expressed in his volume entitled *Duty*. Perhaps the writer's perception of feminine ability is not very different from those husbands who encourage and admire the careers of their wives but also assume that they will provide all the accustomed domestic comfort just the same.

A long journey which Sopwith became used to making after

---

* See chapter 8, p. 81.

Mail Coach c. 1830.

1833 was from Newcastle to the Forest of Dean. The route changed as railway development took place in the decade and his first journey was not itself continuous. On 9th February 1833 he left Newcastle at 9.30 p.m. in the Courier coach which arrived at Boroughbridge at 7 a.m. The coach company provided two post chaises to take the travellers to York which they reached at 10 a.m. He spent time both in the Minster and perambulating in the city, resuming his journey at 6 a.m. on 11th February in the Lord Wellington coach. He had seen the road between York and Tadcaster four times before, so avoiding the worst effects of cold and stormy weather he travelled inside to Leeds, by 9 a.m., a town which he also examined at his leisure, joining others who were making for the Forest of Dean, presumably including John Buddle, his fellow surveyor. At 1 p.m. the Courier coach set out for Sheffield, the road from Wakefield being particularly hilly. Ten of the seventeen passengers alighted at Barnsley to walk through fields and lanes, to the surprise of some elderly inhabitants who mistook them for escaped inmates from Wakefield Asylum. At 6 p.m. they looked down on Sheffield "but it was too closely wrapped in murky clouds of smoke which with the mantle of night enveloped it for us to form any clear idea of its extent or general appearance". After tea at the coaching inn he preferred rest to discovering the town on foot.[7]

The journey "required all possible expedition" so there was ample excuse for not describing Sheffield nor Lichfield nor Birmingham. On 12th February he rose at 5 a.m.and the coach left at 6.30, though not before he took advantage of a stoppage to buy a large cup of coffee for 1½d and an excellent buttered muffin for 2d. He rode the 38 miles to Derby outside, amused by the twisted spire of Chesterfield but not by "the very poor breakfast at the White Lion". Canals were remarked upon and he was surprised how widespread the Trent was permitted to be, seeming "to usurp a most unreasonable area instead of following a narrow bed". With minor regrets at not pausing to see Lichfield, the passengers had a "fine level road and swift horses" to bring them "to that great capital of manufactories, the town of Birmingham". He found it cleaner than Leeds or Sheffield with wide streets and some good shops. They expected to stay a night but found a coach about to leave for Worcester and so departed dinnerless. A long hill out of Birmingham brought them eventually to "Broomsgrove". He evidently had not seen half-timbered black and white houses before. Droitwich seemed very small to have two members in the reformed parliament. At 8 p.m. they arrived at Worcester and found very comfortable quarters at the Unicorn in Broad Street. Shops and houses alike impressed Sopwith who did not omit to visit the Cathedral before continuing his journey. The Gloucester coach left at 10.45 a.m. on the 13th February. He enjoyed the views to the Malverns and over the flooded meadows by the Severn, admiring the village of Kempsey in cider country. The floods were even more evident as the road approached Tewkesbury, ten feet deep with the road only two feet above the water. He sketched an old timbered house in Tewkesbury while horses were being changed. Soon the coach was passing wagons loaded with teazles, a novel sight for him. At 2 p.m. it reached Gloucester. Dinner at the Booth Hall Inn and evensong in the Cathedral was possible before leaving at 5 p.m. and arriving at the market town of Coleford by 8.30 p.m. "Thus we ended a journey which had been fraught with much amusement and accompanied by as large a share of observation as was compatible with the expedition required by the nature of the engagement for which it was undertaken".

The description of the journey from Newcastle to Coleford occupies seventy-three pages of Sopwith's diary. The journey had spread over 4 days and he had inspected four great abbey or cathedral churches en route. The many connections between coaches that had to be made and the lack of a frequent service might have frustrated the traveller but, except perhaps at Sheffield, the young surveyor set out to enjoy all he could see in the time available at each town.

Views on travelling by coach were somewhat dogmatically set out by Sopwith in 1837, the first point being perhaps obvious, the second, on his own admission, apparently ungallant. The occasion was the return from London by Highflyer on Wednesday 26th April with Mr. Fenwick. He had secured two seats on the previous day "with our backs to the horses, a position which every experienced inside traveller well knows the value of". The other inside passenger was a Miss Dunker as he discovered from the Way-bill. Sopwith rode several stages outside with her and gave his philosophy of travel to this "accomplished and agreeable young lady" on her journey to Stamford. The first consideration was health and comfort. Travel within unless the weather or pleasant company merited travelling outside. He observed four maxims. "1st That Ladies have seldom so imperative a motive for travelling as not to be able to defer their journey to a more convenient season. 2nd That where Comfort is a great object the point at issue is not so much the said Lady's health or comfort as the pocket of herself or friends seeing that on all coaching roads a Post chaise may be had and a Gentleman who feels gallant enough to expose himself to cold and wet to oblige a Lady would 'be more prudent' if he paid the expense of her posting instead of a doctor's bill for himself. 3rd That my journeys (which in this year alone exceed 3000 miles) are all on business of moment" and illness would only delay his employer's business, so the inside seat might be regarded as "theirs not mine". A 4th point was that cold and wet at the beginning of a long journey would only bring on his rheumatism and the "welfare and happiness of a Lady at Home is as much the object of my solicitude as that of any stray dames, however fair and accomplished, that may cross my path in my multifarious wanderings". Although Sopwith travelled inside from Stamford after bidding farewell to Miss Dunker, he took good care to order a glass of Brandy Toddy for Mr. Fenwick and himself as soon as Grantham was reached. Standing the driver a glass too, not least to remind him of the order, Sopwith wound his watch, paid the guard for the drivers up till breakfast time and went sound to sleep. He awoke to see the waiter standing at the door with the two glasses of grog. He downed his as if it was a sleeping draught and enjoyed a good sleep until 6 a.m.

On a fourth journey to London within the year 1837 Sopwith not only again enjoyed the company of Mr. Thomas Fenwick, coal-miner and agent for the Bishop of Durham as well as the Dean and Chapter's Collieries, but was thinking "nothing of the journey between Newcastle and London, which once appeared a very serious undertaking. I have learnt to read, to write, and to sleep well on a coach" as well as meet interesting people. The Wellington coach averaged 9 miles an hour, including stoppages except for meals. Leaving at 9.30 a.m., half an hour was allowed for dinner at Northallerton at about 2 p.m., the same at York for tea at 7 p.m.: breakfast was at Grantham soon after 6 a.m., dinner at Harrington about 2 p.m. and arrival at the Bull and Mouth was at 7.30 p.m., 34 hours after the start. The rival Mail took 33 hours up to London and 29 hours back, at £5 and 5 guineas inside respectively. The Wellington inside fare was £4.10.0 and other expenses added on £1.10.0 or more in each case.

A faster journey was one made by express post between Brighton and London on April 18th 1837. From St. Peter's Church Brighton at 3.40 p.m. the first twelve miles were travelled in 54 minutes including 5 minutes for changing horses. On from Hickstead at 4.34 to Crawley (10 miles in 49 minutes), to Red Hill (9 miles in 42 minutes), to Croydon (11 miles in 58 minutes) and so to Westminster Bridge (10 miles in 48 minutes), the post covered the journey of 52 miles in 4½ hours at a cost of £5. 17. 6d. "This may be considered as the maximum speed which can be obtained on post roads without previous and special arrangements".[8]

The earliest railway journey made by Sopwith is not detailed in the surviving diary. Although present as an honoured guest at the jubilee of the Stockton to Darlington line on September 27th 1875

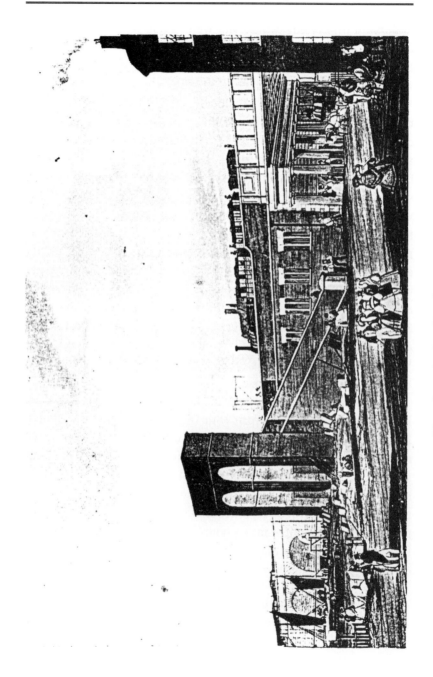

Water Street Station, Manchester 1831.

and recognising that it commemorated the inauguration of the
current system of railway locomotion, it is more likely that he
began rail travel on the Liverpool-Manchester line. The vital diary
is missing. Richardson however states that on March 7th 1833
Sopwith began his journey home from London after his first sortie
to the Forest of Dean. He deliberately went via Manchester in order
to travel by train to Liverpool, so associating himself, only three
years after its inception, with the Liverpool-Manchester railway,
the first full locomotive service of the new era of travel. He caught
the train at 7 a.m. on Saturday 9th March. He characteristically
"minuted the quarter-mile posts and found them as follows: 56",
50", 38", 41", 54", 65", *the whole journey of thirty miles scarcely
occupying two hours*".[9] He returned that evening and went to the
theatre in Manchester before resuming his journey via Leeds,
taking the night coach to Newcastle and arriving home March 12th.

The Liverpool to Manchester line was used a second time in
1834. Before that Sopwith had viewed progress on the Newcastle
to Carlisle line between Newcastle and Hexham on July 16th 1833.
His day began at 3.30 a.m. with writing; he visited his office and
workshops before taking his seven shillings seat on the True Briton
coach to Hexham. The bridges and other works were highly
creditable in his view. If there were any reservations about the
wisdom and usefulness of the line he did not commit them to his
diary. The journey between Liverpool and Manchester however did
provoke comment.

Arriving at Manchester from Burnley in a thick fog, Sopwith
breakfasted at the Palace Inn. Curiously he took the railway
journey very much in his stride but had some reflection on its
comfort. "Nothing particular occurred different to what I had seen
before but three things forced themselves much on my attention.

1. A worse engine than last year

2. More jolting on rails than ditto

3. The vast local improvements along the line

Each of these 'unfold a tale' but I have not time to detail further than remarking, that the enormous expense of good engines and keeping the railway in perfect repair seems indicated by their being both suffered to deteriorate and if such be the case with this railway very few places in the kingdom can afford rapid speed on railways. Horse or engine travelling of 10 or 12 miles an hour is probably the most economical speed and is sufficiently quick for most purposes, but the march of intellect will never rest satisfied with this and they are now scheming a velocity of 40 miles an hour. The immense carriage between Liverpool and Manchester furnishes funds for all manner of experiment and improvement but other poorer concerns must beware ere they attempt to follow the example".[10] The journey was continued by steam packet across the Mersey and by Mail to Chester. If it had been a little disappointing to travel by rail it was nevertheless a practical route for him to take down through Shrewsbury, Hereford and Monmouth to Dean Forest. A rail journey to Maidenhead in July 1839 evoked the comment, "There is a greater amount of lateral vibration in the carriages of this railway (Great Western) than any I have yet travelled upon". These were early days.

At the end of 1839, the diary discloses his general delight of travelling: it agreed well with his health and his strength and spirits seemed to be improving yearly. "Travelling is, to my mind, one of the most interesting occupations that can be pursued during the middle period of life". There was intellectual and physical enjoyment and his professional employment enabled him to combine pleasure with profit. He reflected that he had travelled three thousand miles, mostly in 1838, in two years. In 1840 he would travel 5702 miles, all in Great Britain.

There are few direct references to locomotives or indeed any mechanical details of transport. One such reference occurs in 1840 when the engineer of the Gloucester to Cheltenham line, Captain Moorsom, showed Mr. John Buddle and Sopwith an American engine, the Victoria, No. 84. "It is 8⅓ tons weight and the ratio of the cost, including duty, as compared with English engines, is seventeen to fifteen. The cylinders are outside, and are eleven inches diameter with a twenty-inch stroke. The wheels are four in number, and four feet diameter; they are not coupled". He noted a steep incline from Cheltenham to Cofton where normally two engines drew up trains at 12 m.p.h. or one engine at 6 m.p.h. Sand was needed in wet or frosty weather. There were ten or eleven American engines and four or five English engines on the line. "The iron-plate of the firebox", according to Moorsom, was "not so good as in the English engine, and the tubes should be brass instead of copper". The two mining engineers enjoyed their ride on the footplate at a mean speed of 29 miles an hour over 7 miles.

The opening of the Newcastle to Carlisle railway was by no means as satisfactory as it might have been. The railway had been in use in stages earlier and Sopwith rode on it on April 10th 1838 from Blaydon to Hexham which took 65 minutes. The opening of the whole line from Blaydon to Carlisle, a distance of 60 miles, took place on June 19th 1838. Sopwith wrote the first part of his new diary while in motion and his "example of locomotive manuscript" is perfectly legible if not quite as neat as his usual hand. By page 3 he resorts to pencil.

The railway Company brought out all its engines and a large number of trucks were fitted up with temporary seats for the eager crowds. A procession of 15 trains should have started from Redheugh at 11 a.m. but after many delays and a long stoppage at Blaydon, the procession began at 1.50 p.m. The times and stoppages were faithfully recorded, a sketch of Corbridge made and he reports that the cavalcade duly arrived at Carlisle Basin at 5.33 p.m., 3 hours and 43 minutes later. Sopwith hastened through the crowded streets past the Cathedral to the coffee house where luncheon was provided by the Directors. Despite police efforts to control the crowds he entered with difficulty, the pressure of the crowd being "very annoying". There were three tables down the length of the large Assembly room and one across, at which the

"Mayor of Carlisle presided over this hungry and disorderly assemblage. The Queen's health was drunk with great enthusiasm and followed by three times three cheers of that hearty and cordial gratulation which prevails at feasts in general but especially at gratuitous entertainments. Success to the Railway was received with a similar demonstration of good will. In the mean time I hastily helped myself to some cold beef and bread and after drinking the preceding toasts I went to the Railway Station at the London Road". That was at 6.30 p.m. in the belief that the trains would start at 7 p.m.

The return journey began to move off at last at 10 p.m., most people in open carriages or trucks being soaked by heavy rain. His train reached Redheugh at 3 a.m. next day. Some were as late as 6 or 7 a.m. The waiting families of travellers were thereby much alarmed and the lack of organisation, the discomfort of long waiting and particularly the exposures of a stormy night ride were the topics of conversation for several days. At least there was no accident, no unhappy Huskisson-like tragedy, nor collision.

By June 1844 a new landmark directly affecting Sopwith had occurred in travel by rail: this was the journey from Newcastle to London entirely by train. As recently as April 25th he described a journey combining horse-drawn omnibus and train which he knew to be his last to London using both modes of transport. It had taken 17 hours, including all stoppages, 14½ hours of actual travel at just over 20 miles an hour. The cost was £4.3s.0d. In May he met again Mr. Clegg who was working on the atmospheric railway, a version of which Brunel established south of Exeter: the method of sealing the evacuated tubes by wax and leather unhappily fell foul of hungry rats. On June 19th the great day arrived: "for the first time, the whole railway journey from London to Newcastle was opened to the public". Travelling from Euston, Sopwith arrived at Gateshead 12½ hours later. He recorded the timings in detail.[11]

These were the most significant journeys in Sopwith's early days of travel. There were precarious journeys in Wales, a mammoth

450 mile journey of 48 hours, 37 on the move in 11 different coaches or trains, new ventures in Belgium where he surveyed the Sambre-Meuse line and an ever-widening experience of the pleasure of observing the landscape and gaining business. It is not surprising that he was drawn increasingly to London which provided so many opportunities for new work.

Chapter 8

Visitor to London

The approach to London in 1830 is described in the third small diary written by Sopwith with all the eagerness of a young man, full of self-importance about to descend on the highest court of the land in the metropolis. For the occasion of his visit was the application for an Act of Parliament to construct the Newcastle to Otterburn road. The journey he made by coach was examined again in about 1855 when he had cause to reflect on the different pace and costs of rail travel. The original notes were however written in 1830.

"The first symptoms of London ", as he called them, were the taking of the reins by a gentleman driver, son of a coach proprietor, who in "black dress-coat and top-boots" drove the final 60 miles to London. Sopwith was unimpressed by the Hertfordshire countryside on the chalk with its bare surface and lack of trees: nor was the view an improvement looking from the hill south of Royston. However the weather was clear and sunny and although the cold was piercing on this March day, he eventually travelled on the outside so as not to miss any of "the attractions of the immediate vicinity of London . . . that magnificent city. From sixteen miles from London the road seems one continued country village, with only a few intervening spaces of road for two or three hundred yards. It was dark as we entered the stone-paved streets of London, where the brilliant effect of the gas and the bustle of the people very much corresponded with the idea I had formed of London. At seven o'clock we reached the Bull and Mouth Inn after a journey of

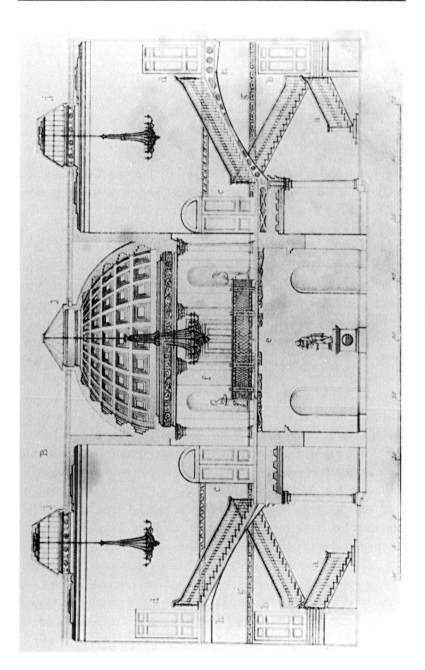

Drury Lane Theatre.

273 miles, performed in 33 hours".[1] After a cup of tea, and consulting his map, he was soon off to see the sights.

St. Paul's Cathedral by moonlight was not as large as he had expected. He immediately compared its size with the dimensions of his beloved St. Nicholas' Church of Newcastle and All Saints' Church. The campanile towers were reported to be 20 feet higher (85 is recorded and then crossed out – a rare error) than the steeples of the two Newcastle churches and the dome 150 feet higher than the great tower of York Minster. Sopwith could not confirm it by observation but continued his walk along Ludgate Hill, down New Bridge Street and along Blackfriars Bridge to Southwark. He walked westward from Blackfriars Road by Stamford Street, "returned to London by Waterloo Bridge, went to Drury Lane Theatre and finally returned to the inn without ever once asking my way or missing my road.

"What a difference a penny makes! Blackfriars Bridge was crowded, Waterloo Bridge seemed, and indeed was at this time, a most delightful and almost unfrequented walk". A peal of eight bells in Southwark reminded him of All Saints, Newcastle, but the Thames' broad surface, "the magnificent front of Somerset House and the heavy gloom that seemed thrown like a mantle over this vast metropolis, excited a train of interesting thoughts, all concentrated in the one vast and comprehensive and inexpressible idea of London!"

Drury Lane was in something of an uproar. Edmund Kean's first appearance as King Henry V had stopped abruptly after four acts. It was 18 minutes before the curtain rose but a great yelling obscured his apology. Breast-striking and appeals to the fair-play of Englishmen saw Act 5 through but the audience was only pacified by a fine performance of Der Freischutz. Sopwith loved the music, especially the laughing and hunting chorus, and found the scenery and stage effects "beyond anything that my imagination could have previously conceived".[2] The description of this and the theatre itself will be left to a later chapter.

Next day, Tuesday March 9th, he arose at 6 a.m. and wrote for three hours. He breakfasted in Holborn with Mr. Percival Fenwick and they went to Mr. Bramwell's offices, presumably to look at business or pick up a copy of the documents needed. They looked into the Law Courts and into Lincoln's Inn Hall where they saw the Lord Chancellor, Lord Lyndhurst. "His Lordship was a healthy, vigorous, good-looking man, far from being stricken in years, and seemed by frequently changing his position and looking very indifferent and unconcerned, as if he would willingly hear the end of a long and seemingly very uninteresting story which a learned gentleman was relating to him". Above the judge's seat it was noted was the painting "Paul before Felix" by Hogarth.

Moving out of the inn, Sopwith took lodgings at 42 Wilmington Square, Spa Fields. He called on Mr. Ord MP, patron and friend, of Whitfield Hall and then to see Fenner, agent for the Otterburn Road Bill, in the lobby of the House of Commons. There was time to walk through Westminster Abbey and he was very disappointed. "I speak with humility in anything that has been directed by superior taste and judgement but I cannot help thinking that the interior of the Abbey and King Henry VII's chapel might, at no great expense, be rendered far more beautiful and imposing than it now is". The organ and waxworks were respectively plain and in poor taste, but the monuments were "magnificent and deeply interesting. Deep and powerful and holy are the impressions they are calculated to make" and he was moved to be amongst the memorials of "the greatest, wealthiest, worthiest and most learned and able men that adorn the annals of our country". He approved of being charged 15 pence to keep out the rabble and here he found the slab with "George Canning" inscribed on it as well as the fine design of Lady Nightingale's memorial. After visiting Mr. Topham in Bermondsey he returned by London Bridge, seeing the new one due to replace it and having a "keek at the pearl o' the City, St. Paul's", before settling down by a good fire with his maps, books and papers. This gave him as much or even more "real peace and true enjoyment than the gayest and most splendid fascinations" which had yet attracted his notice.[3]

On March 10th after writing and breakfasting he hired a hackney for an hour and made various calls before going to the 10 o'clock service at St. Paul's. The organ was magnificent but despite the greatness of the interior, he could not attune himself to the choir and was convinced that "Grecian or Roman architecture is incapable of the solemn and venerable character so peculiar to the Gothic Style". Further calls took him to Southwark Bridge where he spent an hour with a Miss Scott at her father's in Thames Street. He later visited St. Paul's again in her company but as with so many of his acquaintances in London, identification is difficult. Her father was Mr. John Scott but he was not Sopwith's future father-in-law. Sopwith went to listen to the Appollonicon, a form of very large organ. He described it, its makers and its tone. His tour of pleasure took him on to Pall Mall and Regent Street and so to Regent's Park where he saw the Diorama and Colosseum before walking round the park and returning for tea. He spent the evening writing.

The diorama showed him the interior of St. Peter's Rome, interesting to compare with St. Paul's, seen on the same day. Regent Street, of course, came in for criticism for its mere stucco and bore poor comparison to the northern capital of the Scotch. If the Diorama was fine, the Colosseum was marvellous. Here in the polygonal building he saw the panoramic representation of London as seen from St. Paul's top, covering nearly an acre of canvas. Up to twenty people could enter a machine to ascend to the first gallery. The accuracy of the painting fascinated him. "The first sight of it is calculated to create, and does almost invariably create, much astonishment. An Irish gentleman who came in when I was there enquired several times if the dome below us was that which he had seen from outside; when assured that it was not, and that it was in the interior of the building, nothing could exceed his amazement. Gazing with convinced but wondering eyes, he involuntarily exclaimed, 'Lord God Almighty! is it possible?' A testimony of his wonder which, though very objectionable, seemed a most unfeigned expression of the very highest surprise and admiration". Thus did the diarist reflect something of his own admiration while being less naive about the construction inside the Colosseum.

On Thursday 11th March he again made several calls and saw much of West London. His only important business was getting four postage franks from Mr. Ord M.P. On Friday he met Mr. Percival Fenwick, and Mr. Clennell as well as calling upon Mr. Bell in Wimpole Street before attending the House of Commons Committee in the smoking-room. The Committee was attended by Sir M.W. Ridley, Messrs Ellison, Liddell, Bell, Ord and R.F. Wilson. In the chamber, Ord recommended that he should sit in the front of the Strangers' gallery. Here he gained the grim disappoint-ment that many have had observing the operation of the House of Commons. He gave a detailed description of the "plain ordinary-looking place" and of the apparent lack of interest by the speaker during the Gloster and Avon railway bill. "All of a sudden there was a bustling noise and several members walking out with 'Walk out, gentlemen, quick, walk out, walk out'". A division took place: the gallery was cleared. It all seemed farcical but did not create much amusement. "Every now and then Mr. Speaker rose and quickly repeated a brief form of words, to which not one of the members seemed to be paying the least attention". The sentence announced was, "you that are of the opinion that this Petition be received say AYE, you that are of a contrary opinion say NO; THE AYES HAVE IT," Stated at top speed, the speaker was soon through 18 to 20 petitions.

The antics of the House were not all bad. Lord Lowther spoke with "ease and gracefulness . . . that courteous and dignified address which so well becomes a British senator and one who may in time be one of the chiefest nobles in the land". Sopwith left the gallery and missed Liddell's introduction of the Northumberland petition. He preferred to return home to Wilmington Square and the tranquillity of books and papers.

The London visit continued next day at the Monument which he ascended and then with Miss Scott "spent some time in seeing the Monument and other treasures of the great lion of London Lions, St. Paul's. Every visit to this stupendous and magnificent structure increases my admiration of it". How right it was to inscribe 'Circumspice!' on Sir Christopher Wren's monument. Leaving Miss Scott by a warm fire in the library, he ascended to the whispering gallery and up into the ball. It reminded him of the rises in the lead mines "and the civilities (eighteen pennyworth) of my conductor as forcibly called to my remembrance the friendly admonition of the miners, 'Take care, maister, and dinna fall down the rise!'" Models, clock, bell and crypts or vaults were all visited, "the pocket sweating pretty freely all the while; though, after all, when the great convenience of constant attendance on visitors is considered, I do not think the charges exorbitant".

The vaults of St. Paul's gave a solemn effect of deep and heavy gloom which he welcomed after the "sight-seeing' . . . [of] one bright and magnificent and attractive object succeeding another" which produced a sort of vacancy of the mind. The vaults on the other hand gave "mournfully pleasing and interesting associations": the sarcophagus of Nelson, the tomb of Collingwood, "the little spot wherein is laid the rearer of this mighty fabric" all impressed him with contemplations upon the destiny of man. He liked the contrast of the grandeur above and the mouldering ashes below, "the gay and stirring crowds that throng around and in this great temple, and the darkness, and silence and loneliness of these chambers of the dead, eloquently and fervently proclaim the truths which, above all others, the living should lay to heart".

Service-tasting occupied Sopwith's Sunday morning, St. Paul's during the musical part and off to Bishopsgate for a sermon. However the Hon. and Revd. Edward Grey was not preaching there but at St. Sepulchre in Snow Hill. Sopwith arrived just in time at the start of the service: the sermon was for the benefit of a Girls' Charity School, "the scholars of which sat in the organ gallery . . .

in their simple attire . . . with sweet and modest looks, seemed like cherubs sent to awaken compassion in the hearts of men". He was overcome by the sweet singing of the lovely babes for whom a hymn had been specially composed. He shed tears. "My heart earnestly responded (to) that benediction of our Saviour, 'of such is the Kingdom of Heaven'."[4] What would the Reverend John Hodgson have made of these protestations of religion?

Mr. Grey was well up to expectations, solemn and powerful as befitted "a Messenger of God, a Legate of the skies". A lasting influence from the perfect model of pulpit oratory was claimed but the substance is not given to us. Sopwith went to Southwark to dine: his father had stood as sponsor or godfather for Mr. Topham's eldest child and now he, Thomas, was to stand sponsor for the youngest. Although there was a numerous and intelligent party of friends, he begged to be excused after tea and returned to his books and papers.

On Monday he took a letter, of recommendation perhaps, to Mr. Barber at the British Museum who procured him a ticket for the Reading rooms. He had hoped to do some copying for Mr. Hodgson but it was an occasion for looking round on that day and he duly admired the King's Library. He wandered through the museum, longing for a week to take it all in and an intelligent friend to talk to in the Gallery of Sculptures. After dinner at the Café Colosseum, he attended the committee at the House of Commons for the Cowgate Road bill. He also fitted in evensong at the Abbey on this and other occasions when required at the House of Commons.

Other visits made were to Mr. Martin's* establishment at 104 Holborn where he admired the finest lithographs that he had ever seen, quite as good as copper-plate etching. He returned home from the House of Commons by a circuitous route to acquaint himself

---

* This was presumably John Martin, painter, the most stable but nonetheless creatively imaginative, of three brothers. The deranged Jonathan who had set fire to York Minster was a second brother. William, the third brother, set his mind and lost it on perpetual motion and the philosophy of outer space.

with Vauxhall Bridge, Belgrave Square and Hyde Park. By this means he became familiar with much of West London, marking his progress on a map so as to take in the most interesting streets and squares. He took a small boat to Greenwich one morning, admiring the two London Bridges, noticing the alarming rapids at the Old Bridge through which he shot like an arrow. The miles of active commerce with "ships, wharves, docks, warehouses and manufacturers fill the mind with almost over-powering ideas of the greatness of the British Empire". He had an errand to fulfil. His old mentor Henry Atkinson had a brother-in-law, Mr. Riddle who was the Master of the Naval school and another fine mathematician. Sopwith was taking the writings in manuscript of his late schoolmaster to Mr. Riddle. He dined with him before returning to the House of Commons at 3 p.m. There he was informed by the parliamentary agent that he was no longer needed in London.

The enthusiasm for London continued on subsequent visits but the first excitement of travel to it was not repeated. When he was summoned to the House of Lords Committee for Wednesday 24th March he had hardly time to attend the funeral of his uncle James before travelling back to the city. He did ride for 6 miles outside near Doncaster but otherwise was glad to read or sleep for the whole journey. Back in town he breakfasted and bathed at Spa Fields, showing no weariness and continued his enjoyment of London as before.

Chapter 9

London Business and Acquaintance

London life for Sopwith was divided up with as much enjoyment of business and pleasure as before, but as he gradually came to know the city better and who else might be visiting or at home, he extended his range of acquaintance and the opportunities for acquiring knowledge. If he thirsted for acquaintance he also saw opportunities to enlarge the market for his own interests, a market of ideas and their practical application.

On his second visit to the city Sopwith visited the National Repository of Arts. Here he saw inflatable globes, Rolff's patent self-acting pianos, many models, sculptures and plans, both useful and amusing. Here too on show was Chevalier Aldini's fireproof clothing: it was of strong woollen cloth, soaked in saline and covered with an armour of wire gauze. He wanted some better mathematical instruments and found an improved version of a pentegraph. He had on his first trip purchased a very good microscope at Bithrays and some instruments at Troughton and Simms: this latter firm would be a useful outlet for him three years later. At Ackermanns he bought several colours for use in sketching and plans. On a visit to the Guildhall he admired the monuments of Alderman Beckford, Nelson, Chatham and Pitt as well as Hogarth's tale of the idle and industrious apprentice in another company hall. He soon settled into the routine of a bath at Spa Fields and a good meal at the Colosseum: the mock turtle soup was a favourite. He so liked the setting that he asked permission to sketch the place and its furniture.

The Horse Guards.

There came an opportunity one day to see the king's entrance to the House of Lords and it was here that the indefatigable lion-hunter saw one of the finest specimens. As Sopwith and his companion gazed at the spacious corridors and scagliola columns, "only one person passed by us – he was plainly dressed in a blue surtout and walked through the House of Lords". Mr. Fenner bowed to him and Mr. Sopwith would gladly have gazed and reflected upon him for an hour: it was the Duke of Wellington. "So rare a Lion in so splendid a place was certainly interesting" and he recalled that other Lion seen in his setting, Sir Walter Scott.[1] That the visitor was unable to write anything more voluble is strange at a stage in his life when he was impressionable and the diary entry original, but the sight of the soldier-statesman in "the grandest part of the British Senate house" was commendation enough.

The links which he had through lead mining with the Greenwich Hospital gave an introduction not only to Edward Hawke Locker, former secretary and now Commissioner, but also John Taylor F.R.S. for whom he had produced drawings of mining plans from Alston. Mr. Taylor invited him to see his collection of plans and minerals: Sopwith knew a good contact when he saw one. He not only respected Mr. Taylor as one of the "principal Mining Men in the kingdom" which "necessarily rendered me anxious to avail myself of his polite attentions" but he also received a note of introduction to Mr. Lonsdale "the curator of the Geological society". The magpie in him enjoyed looking at "Cosmoramas, Dioramas and Physioramas" all one afternoon, pictures magnified with or without further lenses and with very interesting movements. After that the Oxford Street bazaar provided a large number of pick-nick articles, superintended by pretty girls who almost bewitched the money from any passer-by venturing to bargain. A Mr. Davison – was he Robert Davison of Hill & Davison, organ-builders? – showed him fine designs for rails and gates on which Davison was engaged for a smithery in Old Street.

As well as observing trade and commerce, a visit to the Bank of England itself provided a fascinating morning on 27 March 1830 where he looked into numerous offices. A further visit to Greenwich Hospital caused Sopwith to wonder at one of the finest, most magnificent, most uniform and extensive structures of the kind in Europe.[2] He described it as a "city of palaces", passing from the hall strangely quickly to the chapel with its great organ, the richness of the chapel being compared with the cost of re-building the whole of All Saint's church Newcastle. The former had cost £60,000, the latter some £27,000. He viewed His Majesty's "Old Game Cocks" at dinner and saw into the kitchens. Here an old tar gave him some particulars of what was cooked in three great cauldrons and on the open fire grate: 5 cwt of potatoes steamed for three quarters of an hour; 7 cwt of meat (8 cwt on Sunday) for about an hour and a quarter, four days mutton and three days beef. At the grate, 20 or 30 lbs of meat were roasted for the petty officers who chose it. The cauldron for hot drinks held 180 gallons made up from 45 lbs of cocoa and 42 lbs of sugar in the morning with 8 lbs of tea and 36 lbs of sugar in the evening. On remarking to one old veteran how comfortable the pensioners must be he received the reply, "Aye true, Sir, they're all well enough, but then we deserve it, ye see, or else we wouldn't have been here".[3] Sopwith liked the wisdom noted on the printed board in the dining-room.

Counsel and advice

Hear		to be silent
Be Silent	*and learn*	to understand
Understand		to remember
Remember		to practise

	see, judge	
All that you	hear, believe	*it not!*
	know, tell	
	can do, do	

Before you speak – think!

and regard well

What you speak, where you speak,
of whom you speak and to whom you speak

	Religion		lose	
By	Generosity	*you*	impoverish	*not*
	Injustice		enrich	
	Wickedness		profit	

	Property, some	
If you lose	Health, much	*is lost*
	Reason, more	
	Your soul, all	

Such homely sound sense struck familiar chords in a would-be educator. After a thoroughly enjoyable fine day with two hours in the park and a sail on the Thames at high water he returned to dine with Mr. Locker at 5 p.m., spending the evening with him and finding a mind captive to ideas on mining plans and practice.

In danger of hearing the wrong preacher again, Sopwith slipped out just in time to hear Mr. Irving at the Foundling Hospital on Sunday March 28th before availing himself for 3 hours of Mr. Taylor's plans and minerals which directed him to "profound and heartfelt and humble adoration of God".[4] He had an introduction from W.C. Trevelyan to the zoo and marvelled at the romantic impression given by the Swiss Cottage. "In the level plain of Regents part (sic) a well manged (sic) excavation with cascades

etc. impresses a belief that the spectator is in the midst of the most
lone and deep and rocky and precipitous recesses of mountain
scenery". Later he would enjoy a man-adapted but more natural
gorge at Armstrong's Jesmond Dene home. The pace of his diary
became a little more frantic before his impending return to Newcastle: there were visits to Mr. Pratt, Mr. Baber at the British
Museum, Boosey's music shop in Holles Street, Thomas Phillips,
Professor of Painting, about Sir John Swinburne's portrait, and the
papier mâché factory in Edgware Road. He may have been considering using papier mâché for geological models, similar to one of
France exhibited by him in the 1838 British Association exhibition
in Newcastle.[5] A call on Mr. William Ord of Whitfield was
followed by a visit to the Zoo Museum in Bruton Street and to the
Society of British Artists Exhibition, all too quickly, before seeing
real lions fed at the Royal Menagerie now at Charing Cross
("removed from Exeter change") and buying a pantographer. At
Covent Garden he heard "The Messiah". The next day saw him at
the Excise office in Broad Street, the museum of East India House,
where he was fascinated by Eastern manuscripts, and continuing
his animal observations at the Tower but deferring a visit to the
armouries and jewels. The journey back to Newcastle, as well as
being cold with snow on the ground, no longer held the magic of
his first visit.

A new stage of Sopwith's career began with an important
appointment to which he had almost certainly been recommended
by John Buddle, the great Tyneside colliery viewer. Buddle himself
came with the news on 3rd February 1833, bringing the official
letter from Mr. Alexander Milne of the Department of Woods and
Forests confirming Thomas Sopwith's appointment as Commissioner to survey the Forest of Dean. Buddle and Probyn were the
other two members of what proved to be a speedy and successful
undertaking and one which took Sopwith frequently to London.
The first call on the Department of Woods and Forests was not
originally intended, as will be related later: a leading coal-owner,

Mr. Edward Protheroe, had been most obstructive. However it coincided with further work of the Committee on the Derwent Road and was an essential reassurance that his commission had the full backing of His Majesty's Department of Woods and Forests.

In 1834 he renewed acquaintance with Mr. Robert Davison, organ builder, and met Mr. Wright of the Atlas office, a North Countryman whose hospitality, wit and genius Sopwith appreciated over the years. As well as visiting the Department of Woods and Forests, attending railway committees and giving evidence on the Newcastle Waterworks Bill, he was able to show his young surveying assistants, Marcus Scott and William Woods, some of the sights he had enjoyed on previous visits. He went to a meeting of the Institute of Civil Engineers of which he had become a member in the previous year. On a later visit he was eliciting help from William Ord M.P. for Mr. Peter Nicholson, "the eminent Architectural and Mathematical writer", who had fallen on hard times and for whom a subscription was being raised, largely by Northumbrian figures. He met Mr. Gordon, a Secretary of the Treasury, but on what they discoursed it is difficult to say. Mr. Gordon evidently made it plain what difficulties were faced by the leading departments of government.

The diary Sopwith kept is not very full between 1834 and 1837 but 1836 was undoubtedly a very busy year. An important law case, Clayton vs Gregson, was in progress to determine the construction to be put on the word "level" in a lease of coal under a property. He and Buddle, together with Nicholas Wood of Newcastle, travelled all the way across to Wigan to view the place concerned. The case was settled in Liverpool and doubtless he and his companions were anxious to hear the legal reasoning behind the decision which might have affected their own professional interests all over the country. He himself was to be involved in the Harrogate Sulphur Wells case in 1837 along with such distinguished witnesses as John Dalton, William Smith, regarded as "fathers" of chemistry and geology respectively, Professor Daniell, Professor John Phillips,

John Buddle, Professor Johnstone, chemist, Mr. John Johnstone of Edinburgh, Dr Clanny of Sunderland and Mr. West, a Leeds chemist. Sopwith used a model to explain to the advocate Cresswell the geological details.[6]

London acquaintance in 1836 included meeting Mr. Fisher the eminent publisher and afterwards hearing Mr. John Martin, the artist of apocalyptic taste*, explaining his plans for improving the River Thames. This was set forth in a paper to the Institution of Civil Engineers. Sopwith continued to work hard on the Great North of England railway, using the express coach to reach London with vital evidence to confound opponents to the scheme.

Sopwith's fourth visit to London was briefly delayed by an urgent request by Mr. Morton, the Earl of Durham's agent, to show round a visiting Russian general, Count St. Aldegonde.† The Count hoped that he would call on Sopwith in London at Woods Hotel, time permitting. The increasing cosmopolitan experience may also be measured by the acquisition of many books. Amongst those sent to be bound by Sopwith at this time were 45 volumes of the *London Encyclopedia*. He seems to have been prosperous and able to build up a considerable library. The sale catalogue of the books from his Westminster home is extant: it shows his wide scientific taste and somewhat narrower artistic preferences. In the same year, 1837, he also had his portrait painted by Mr. James Ramsay whose work he had seen earlier in the year at the Royal Academy. Here he had admired Ramsay's portrait of Earl Grey but thought little of the rooms in which the paintings were hung.

It was necessary to buy a hat when he arrived in London: he had left his usual hat behind back in Newcastle. He put up at Woods Hotel as was now usual and set about business both with his assistant surveyor, Mr. Charles Brumell, and with Mr. Fenwick. He valued the latter's opinion on the question of some Durham mine

*   See p. 88 note
†   See ch 6.

leases, a report on which had been sent to the Chancellor of the Exchequer. Fenwick's agency with both the Dean and Chapter and the Bishop of Durham made him an authority. But it was for the London and Brighton Railway that Sopwith had originally come. Tithe Commutation plans were also under discussion and the Dean Forest Bill needed his attention: Mr. Garner, Solicitor to the Office of Woods, explained that mining and enclosure departments would probably be separated. Sopwith heard the Great North of England Railway Bill being approved and commented in passing that the plans made in his office were on stout paper five feet wide and 227 feet long! The cost of the bill was £450,995, the Yorkshire section was 41 miles and 46 chains long: there were 61 bridges and 27 culverts. He prepared himself for the giving of evidence, regretting delays but was able to use the time examining the ordnance maps of Ireland of 6 inches to the mile, valuable but not clear enough in his view, as well as speaking to Walker, the cartographer and map seller, about his maps, hoping that Walker would use Smith's and Phillips' geological information. His account of the evidence showed both a firmness on his part and inaccuracy of others on the reporting of it.

The London and Brighton railway surveys had been an expensive exercise, so much so that Sopwith had been courteously told by Mr. Coates that he had overcharged by £93.5s.0d. Apart from a clerical error of £9.9s.0d. by Coates, Sopwith not unnaturally felt it necessary to defend himself. He wrote in some detail what the expenses were and said that he would be happy to abide by Mr. Cubitt's* decision, or indeed that of Mr. Provis, Mr. Fearon or Mr. Coates himself if he would look further at the details. Mr. Coates happily accepted the state of affairs and apologised for being wrong. The subject of a general Tythe (sic) survey was also discussed with Mr. Blamire and Lieutenant Dawson, but the Committee on the Tithe surveys shrank from the expense. Sending his assistant off by steam packet to Newcastle, Sopwith stayed a

---

* Afterwards Sir William Cubitt, railway and building contractor.

further day to discuss Sir Edward Blackett's Westwater Manors, suggesting that Dr William Smith the geologist should look at them.

The sixth visit to London was concerned with Dean Forest affairs. His first cousin, James' son Thomas, came in lieu of Joseph Dickinson, together with five other assistant surveyors and clerks. Further business matters related to the Great North of England railway and Sir Edward Blackett's manors. Mr. Milne of the Department of Woods took Buddle and Sopwith off to Henley, a trip enlivened by Buddle's anecdotes and a perusal of Smith's Section of the Strata, part of the collection of Smith's geological plans and maps which Sopwith had bought and which had been autographed by William Smith himself. Milne was of course needed to strengthen the hands of the Dean Forest surveyors and travelled with them to meet the difficult Mr. Edward Protheroe, a considerable proprietor who was not entirely silenced.[*]

Back in London, after an enjoyable stop at Oxford and a short meeting with Dr Buckland, Sopwith had banking business at Glyn's and a visit to Mr. Cubitt's house. Here Cubitt's new desk, similar to a davenport, was admired and so was the gas lighting. The lack of smell of the twenty-five lamps to be found in the rooms and on the staircases was a marvel to him: the cost of running them was about £25 a year. In the House of Commons meanwhile Lord John Russell's motion for a Committee of Enquiry on Church Leases was being debated. Sopwith discovered later from Mr. Bethune of the Home Office that his name was on the Speaker's list for this.

Newcastle business was under discussion on 13th June 1837. Mr. Ord enabled Mr. Donkin to have an interview with the speaker to reduce obstructions to the progress of the Newcastle Improvement Bill. In a visit to the Royal Academy, despite the crush, Sopwith admired Chantrey's statue of Dalton, Bailey's sculptures and Ramsay's portrait of Earl Grey. At a party at Woods hotel Mr. Donkin

* See Chapter 11

included Buddle and Sopwith who met Bailey and Ramsay there. By October 1837, Ramsay was painting Sopwith's portrait which may be the small canvas showing a confident young man seated in an upright armchair with a book and papers beside him, a portrait still in the possession of the family.

By 1837 Sopwith was enjoying the society of the foremost geologists of the day at the Geological Society and of the more exclusive Geological club, most satisfying to his vanity and his genuine scientific interest. However his sense of duty caused him to abandon visiting the British Association meeting at Liverpool in favour of more detailed explanations to Mr. Milne to save a long correspondence. This would have disappointed Sopwith but he was not one to put duty aside however much other interests tempted him. Discussions with Milne included the question of making a model, a suggestion of Buddle's, to explain the veins and workings of Dean Forest.* Details of when the Dean Forest bill would be available being made known and the deposition of certain plans being completed, there was time for a visit to St. Paul's before return to Newcastle, well satisfied both with the progress of his career and with a widening circle of friends and interests.

* Chapter 14, p. 193.

Chapter 10

Religion, Music and Entertainment

The consideration of three such abiding interests as religion, music and entertainment in Thomas Sopwith's life in a single chapter needs some defence. The pivot of the three is music. If at first glance there seems little connection between religion and entertainment, and perhaps none to Sopwith himself, there is nevertheless observation and enjoyment in his practice of religion which suggests entertainment. Entertainment is after all not merely what may divert or amuse, but what gives pleasure and satisfaction and at its best, inspiration. It is easy enough to see how religion and music were linked together for him: music and entertainment were similarly parts of a whole picture of both domestic and public pursuit richly appreciated.

Did religious belief cause anxiety for Sopwith? It is tempting to think that religion at large did not trouble him. It was important in a practical way, he partook of it readily and had little doubt of the blessings of an almighty God. He was helped by his friend the Reverend Anthony Hedley who had married Sopwith and Mary Dickinson and with whom he shared an interest in local Alston mining history. Hedley, at nearby Whitfield, was probably a principle comforter to the distraught young widower who faced Mary's death of 28th July 1829. The particular chapter of Sopwith's diary is missing. B. W. Richardson refers to the missing chapter as "one of the most touching narratives I ever remember to have read".[1] In it there was an account of the correspondence between husband and wife, of the trust they put in each other, their mutual fondness for music and the details of the catastrophe: two days after the birth of Jacob, named after Thomas' father, Mary laughs too vigorously and needs to be calmed. Terrible internal pains ensue which last through until Tuesday July 28th. With Thomas and her parents at the bedside she dies in the afternoon. Thomas needed religion to comfort him at that point in his life and although he sought a firm discipline of walking, working, eating and sleeping as cheerfully as possible, he was surely deeply touched by those qualities of life which are recorded as a memorial to Anthony Hedley. Those phrases which stand out literally in larger capital letters in the memorial were some that commended themselves to Sopwith. There was a "sincerity, industry and efficiency rarely equalled" with much time devoted "TO VISITING AND INSTRUCTING THE POOR AT THEIR OWN HOUSES", as well as "regular personal superintendence to the education of the children IN THE SEVERAL PAROCHIAL SCHOOLS". In the pulpit he was a "clear, eloquent and practical EXPOUNDER OF DIVINE TRUTH, suiting his discourses to the circumstances and capacity of his hearers . . . EXEMPLIFYING . . . the character of a faithful and apostolical SERVANT OF JESUS CHRIST . . . AS A HUSBAND, FATHER AND A MASTER . . . HONORED (sic) AND BELOVED".[2] Along with many other attributes, Hedley had that wise, intelligent and caring character[3] which was expected but not always found amongst clergymen.

The Bishop of Durham whose lack of interest in details of railways or the young surveyor's enthusiasm in depicting plans of the new routes, can hardly be blamed for a hasty dismissal of the railway plans. So also did Parson Routh, President of Magdalen College Oxford, have considerable difficulty in appreciating that a visitor from Essex would no longer be prevented from winter travel on roads across the sticky, sodden clays of that county because of a new form of transport, the railway. It was Sopwith's perception of what a bishop should be like which took a knock. To "one of

St. Nicholas Steeple, Newcastle.

the humblest of the flock", the great bishop seemed no gentleman and a poor shepherd. Of Sopwith himself the Reverend John Hodgson had said "he pretends to be all humility and full of religion", but in a forgiving mood, Sopwith later gave a more balanced view of Bishop Van Mildert. This appears in a note at the end of the diary, apparently written in the same year. In it he speaks of the general character of Van Mildert as a man of great mildness, "commended for gentleness and kind feeling, nor have I ever allowed a recollection of the incident to lessen my respect for his general conduct and extensive charities". Another on a similar errand had found the bishop difficult, but it must be supposed that the abrupt behaviour "arose from some nervous irritability . . . a mere temporary exception to the ordinary tenour (sic) of his general conduct".[4] Who can guess what evaluation of the Bishop of Bath & Wells might have been made had direct introduction taken place. The porter at the bishop's palace gate offered in answer to Sopwith's enquiry whether the bishop was a pleasant man to talk to, "O Lord love you sir, to hear him talk you would think he was God Almighty". This, it is recorded, was the highest praise from his informant, despite its impropriety.

Observation of the clergy, a class or two above the craftsman-surveyor and with whom he sought to mingle on equal terms, hardly reveals his own religious sensibility. Furthermore the careful discretion of his diary, the absence of early volumes and the general sense of fair play leave us all too little idea of his deeper feelings. The nearest approach to religious sentiment, apart from the many hours enjoyed in the organ loft of St. Nicholas' cathedral or listening to choral services in other great churches, may be sought in "Evening, lines written at Alston Moor, November 1825." He was sufficiently proud of these to have them printed and published by Davison of Alnwick.[6] The opening lines do not promise great poetry:-

'I love at EVEN-TIDE to view
The western sky's deep reddening hue,

And calm advancing shades of night,
And sadness of slow fading light
Until the evening shades have chas'd
The sun behind the dark blue waste;'.

Looking down on the stream which "Northumbria's sons may love to trace" and across the barren moors of Alston, he is led to religious language: "holy energies", "reflection's holy power", "heavenly light" and the contemplations of the soul rise

'From this dull earth to vaulted skies,
Studded with glorious worlds around,
Where greatness and goodness for ever abound.'

so that the burdened soul may find rest. Evening, the verse goes on to say, is a picture of universal doom, bringing to a close energies and brightness. In the final two stanzas, Friendship is addressed as the quality which with divine faith will emerge "reigning in realms of light"; but ultimately it is Nature itself which speaks to the writer,

'No sound falls on the listening ear,
But the voice of glorious hosts of the skies,
And the anthems of Nature's vast works that arise
From the murmuring streams and the slow waving trees
Borne softly along on the slow passing breeze.'

The verses hover between the ordered certainties of day and night, celebrated in the noble poetry of Addison, and the romantic respect of Wordsworth, in awe of nature: but they lack the power of either and although Sopwith always acknowledged the beauty and beneficence of the natural landscape about him, it was there to

be measured, assessed, evaluated and even conquered in the service
of man, the recipient of the Creator's gifts.

Religion, it was often stated in his diary, ought to be practical.
Its practicality should be expressed both in the shape of the church
where it occurred and through the honest sermons of common-
sense clergymen. The former views are easily traced to Sopwith's
Principles of Design, published in the *Architectural Magazine*
edited by his energetic friend John Claudius Loudon. Loudon's
amazing output on plants and gardening was never quite matched
in his architectural writings. His interest in design touched a chord
in Sopwith who is boldly designated in the magazine as "T.
Sopwith Esq. F.G.S. Architect." His ideas must have derived in part
from the new church built by David Stephenson for All Saints,
Newcastle with its open line of sight to the holy table and pulpit
and its elliptical form. Thus the principles of design chosen were
first, fitness and economy, second, fitness and beauty, with regard
to the ornament, and third, to inspire devotional feeling. "The day
of cathedrals is gone past", and it was no longer necessary to make
room for processions nor a large space for adoration of images,
though he feared that design was too often imitative of past ideas.
All should see and hear the preacher. Pew no 37 which Sopwith
took in St. Nicholas, Newcastle in 1843 was evidently only like a
foot in the door. He took it on trial for a year, hoping that a better
one would become available. Aisles might be a nuisance and he
remarked that some of the best places to sit in cathedrals were those
places reserved for the poor as he had himself experienced when
hearing the Bishop of Hereford. A sermon should be preached too
and not read, as he once experienced at St. Margaret's, Westminster.[7] The hearer should be able to look directly towards the
preacher, again suggesting a semi-circular auditorium. However a
second article for Loudon shows a greater appreciation of a church
as more than a preaching-house.

It was important for Sopwith that a cathedral church should be
adapted to protestant worship in a number of ways. Space for

worshippers was paramount; a height of 20 to 25 feet was sufficient and the walls should present a boldly-carved, near uniform surface to prevent dispersion of sound, avoiding recesses for windows and doors; the pulpit should have an arched canopy so as not to lose sound above it, nor should it be too far forward from the altar or communion table, but near the east wall or screen at one side of the choir; the temperature should be cool in summer and moderately warm in winter; side aisles and transepts should be seen as galleries for monuments, which they have largely become; notice of the preachers and music to be played should be set on a board as at St. Paul's; sermons and music and art should be once again appreciated. He was sure that Wren would have done better at St. Paul's had materials and the confidence of his masters given him a freer hand.

If Sopwith's religious sensibilities were aroused by music in the great cathedral church of Durham, which was his first favourite, his beliefs probably followed a practical common sense approach which might broadly be dubbed latitudinarian. Not averse to enquiry into hypnotism or spiritism, he ventured to see whether they had any worth and remained sceptical of them. As far as preaching was concerned, the preacher was part of the message: if he was honest, so was his message. This conclusion was arrived at only gradually and the occasion on which the Honourable and Reverend Edward Grey preached at St. Sepulchure's, Snow Hill caught at least as much at Sopwith's heart and sense of deference as it did his head. In his first enthusiastic visit to London he had already attended a service at St. Paul's on Sunday 14th March 1830 when he went to Bishopsgate to hear Grey. Learning that Grey was at St. Sepulchre's, he rushed there and found a place just as the service was starting. As already recorded* he was deeply affected. "Chaste, and simple, and dignified, and expressive, the sermons of Mr. Grey seem to me as almost perfect models of pulpit oratory – at least I

---

* See chapter 8

can truly say that his sermons more than any other I ever heard, have had a lasting influence on my mind, and some of his eloquent passages seem indelibly impressed on my memory".[8] Of the content, nothing is recorded. Nor do we know what his views were on Evangelical preaching except that after one sermon identified as of that origin there was "a long controversial discourse . . . till after midnight"[9] with Mrs Hodgson* and a Miss Rawes on July 17th 1833. Since he attended service at the Roman Catholic chapel at Leith Walk, near Edinburgh, on July 21, it may be presumed that his approach to church services was truly catholic. When he attended the Roman Catholic Chapel of the Bavarian Ambassador in Warwick Street, he heard a sermon on the doctrine of the Trinity monotonously delivered. He could not detect "anything at variance with the usual discourses of the clergy of the Establishment on this subject".[10]

One strange preacher disappointed Sopwith when he was back at Alston in 1837. At the Independent chapel with Mr. Dickinson he heard Dickinson's relative, Mr. Scott, tutor of Airedale College, give in broad Northumbrian a sermon "attempting to prove as reasonable many points which every sensible and reflecting mind must be convinced are beyond the reach of reason". Reason could not be the foundation of faith, but knowledge would lead to "a more rational and exalted piety . . . and God will be truly worshipped by the offering of gratitude for his blessings and of admiration for the Wonder of his works".[11] Sopwith's wider knowledge of sermons heard in London was perhaps distancing him from the simpler chapel background of Alston. Impracticality again struck him on hearing a forty minute sermon on the second coming of Elijah, full of biblical criticism on the millennium and far beyond the grasp of the rustic congregation at Longhope, Coleford. The Bishop of Durham's discourse at the re-opening of the repaired Trinity chapel on Sunday October 15th was commended for its appropriate, if

---

* The Revd. John Hodgson does not appear to have been present

short, plainness and practicality. He spoke of "the progress of architecture, the refinements of art and the skill and industry of manufacturing pursuits in this district". Nevertheless a more homely figure was also much admired, a craftsman turned curate, the Reverend Blyth Hurst. Curate of Garrigillgate near Alston, from 1842, Blyth Hurst was a blacksmith from Winlaton who had studied day by day in moments snatched from the anvil. His learning in Hebrew, Greek and Arabic came from his own unaided reading and his ordination was highly approved by the partly self-educated Sopwith. He was zealous, sincere and benevolent and it must have been a relief to find such a man in a remote Pennine parish as Sopwith renewed old friendships in Alston, introducing his second wife Jane to the kindly Dickinsons in 1842. Perhaps his heart was already turning back to the hills so eagerly depicted in his *Account of the Mining Districts*, making it easier to choose his return when the occasion rose in 1845.

Puseyism, as the anglo-catholic revival was often named, did not pass unnoticed. "I bought a catechism abusing the Puseyites and a compendious arrangement of Scripture texts etc." states an 1842 entry.[13] Blyth Hurst wrote a pamphlet called "Christianity no Priestcraft" and a more direct comment occurs in 1843. A new chapel of St. Peters, Newcastle was built. The Revd. William Dodd had raised funds for it and caused both architecture and style of service to be altered to what is now popularly called "Puseyism". This is described as "a rigid adherence to certain forms which had been neglected and a conformity with the views expressed by the authors of a series of tracts entitled *Tracts for the Times* published at Oxford". One such place was St. Andrews, Newcastle where Sopwith enjoyed the "New-man-ia", especially the chanting. He comments that Newman did not have the freedom at St. Mary's, Oxford to practise the semi-Roman Catholicism evident in other places.* Sopwith approved the space for kneeling, the increased

---

* He both bought Tract 90 in 1841 and heard part of a sermon by Newman, but admitted to preferring the company of Buckland and his small daughter looking at the sunset from Magdalen Bridge.

space for the public and the chanted services such as he loved in the cathedrals. Unfortunately the ceremonial observance was not to his liking nor to that of "the steady friends of the reformed church of England".[4] He could likewise appreciate the Reverend Richard Clayton's excellent sermon against the evils of the race course, heard on June 15 1843 at St. Thomas' Church, but feared that the zealous evangelicals must provide other suitable amusements such as museums and botanical gardens for innocent recreation.[15] It was with some sadness then that he reported at Canterbury that the museum was less well known than Felix Summerly's handbook which perpetuated "the memory of old and useless monkish superstitions".[16]

The Roman Catholic religion itself did not attract Sopwith when he encountered it on his visit to Ireland in 1838 but he also had strong views about the evils of the established Church of Ireland being sustained for a minority. As in other religious enquiries, he did not delve behind the theology, although he did ask a Roman Catholic gentleman whether the prayers offered up before the pictures or stations in the Chapel of Glanamarra were to expiate part of the sins of the devout. "It is upon that speculation", was the reply which much amused Sopwith. He generally approved their sincerity, regretted their funerals and found congregations very lively and talkative as soon as the ceremonial was over, or occasionally before it was over. He did not think that the Roman Catholic religion was "adapted to promote the spread of those liberal and enlightened views which are the brightest feature of genuine christianity".[17] Protestantism was surely more likely to promote political freedom, although he did not comment whether this was appropriate in Ireland. He fiercely attacked the illiberalism and folly of the maintenance of the established church in a form which caused nearly 3000 villagers to pay £300 – £400 to a clergyman serving only 10 or 20 persons in a parish, or worse, no church, nor service, nor resident clergyman at all. This only gave a treble premium to

Roman Catholicism: a bad example of desertion of the flock, the Roman Catholic chapel as the sole place of worship and finally the persecution and injustice which Satan himself would turn to his account.

The library of a man of science in the nineteenth century included numerous books signed by other men of science, presented, as Sopwith himself did, as liberally as visiting cards. There were also some books of sermons and other religious works. In the catalogue of books sold after his death we find Blair's sermons, Van Mildert's Bampton lectures and Williams' *Dictionary of All Religions*. There are Bibles, works by the Reverend Baden Powell on the *Unity of Worlds*, the *Order of Nature in Claims of Revelation* but very few works of devotion in the sale of over 700 items. What did he think of the geological discoveries and their effect upon the origins of creation? Did Darwin's *Origins of the Species* shape his faith?

A lecture given to the Leeds Mechanics Institution and Literary Society was partly on "Geology as evidencing Benevolent Design". He had no doubt that "the past events of Geological History strongly confirm the scriptural account of the creation of man [and] of the deluge" and his cited authorities were Dr Hook (an address at Leeds in 1839), Dr Pusey on Genesis 1 and "the high authority of Dr Sumner, Buckland, Sedgwick and other divines".[18] It is probable that he preferred to reflect on God's handiwork in Buckland's *Bridgewater Treatise* of 1836 as befitted a friend and fellow scientist rather than the spiritual or ecclesiastical emphasis put forward by J.H. Newman in the next decade. It is likely that he accommodated much scientific discovery without it shaking a simple trust in the Heavenly Father. To Him family prayers were said.* To Him were committed those of Sopwith's family who died

---

* He started the practice of Sunday evening prayers early in 1843. Reading and explanation of a part of scripture for the improvement of family and servants alike was the central focus, with no desire to interfere with views which the servants might have learned in dissenting chapels.

before him and to Him were given abundant thanks for the blessings of a full and fruitful life year by year.

* * *

Music and music-making remained an absorbing part of life for one
who often played the organ by ear and was equally interested in
the construction of such musical instruments or music-making
machines. An early reference in the extant diary describes a visit
to Norham church where Sopwith "played a voluntary and the
Porteguese (sic) hymn on the organ".[19] He was staying with Mr.
Eliot, owner of the Berwick brewery, who had a barrel organ and
a good piano. A Mr. Smith played and sang at the latter's house
during the evening: there was "Scots wha hae","the harp in Tara's
halls", "Gloomy Winter" as well as Luther's Hymn of Judgement,
Lord Mornington's and other chants. The prize piece for the
delighted Sopwith was the "Storm", "a m.s. piece of music sent by
the composer Beethoven to his present Majesty" in which there was
"a most affecting and sublime imitation of the most awful and most
pleasing dispensations of Providence – the angry rolling waves, the
thunder – the storm – the agonies of despair in a seaman perishing
and in the immediate prospect of death he beholds his wife and
child upon the shore;" but "the waves are stayed – the winds and
seas obey the heavenly voice of their creator . . . and all the
company on board bow down and praise him who ruleth in Heaven
and in Earth and over all".[20]

Rarely does the diarist give such space to a musical evening,
however genial or affecting the occasion. There were plenty such
evenings which gave him much pleasure, especially among old
friends. A social historian of the musical evening could find useful
material for the names of pieces played are often mentioned. But
it was the organ and similar instruments which drew Sopwith like
a bee to honey.

If no cathedral ever exceeded the magnificence of Durham in its structure and music nor any organ-playing replaced the opportunities he had alongside Mr. Ions at St. Nicholas', Newcastle, he nevertheless eagerly sought organs, organists and organ-builders elsewhere. Jonathan Martin's depredations in the choir at York Minster prevented musical appreciation there on Sopwith's southward journey to London in 1830, although much enjoyed in 1833, but in the metropolis itself Westminster and St. Paul's were soon visited. The organ at the former he found plain but on a later occasion found the chanting sweeter than St. Paul's and the anthem well delivered. The organ at St. Paul's, suitable in design to the character of the building, looked less attractive than Durham's, but he admitted he could not judge the relative musical merits, although he loved the deep and solemn chords.

The real excitement in the world of organs was the Appollonicon by Flight and Robson which he saw at their works in St. Martin's Lane. It was in principle "a very large organ with a great variety of pipes and other musical accompaniments which imitate different instruments". It had both "nicety of modulation" and full powers of tremendous effect. There were several sets of piano keys in front enabling five or six performers to play simultaneously. It was thus somewhat larger than the modern synthesiser but equally exciting in its day. The overture to Figaro and to Der Freischutz were performed "by machinery . . . with astonishing brilliancy and to all who have any love for music the Appollonicon can scarcely fail to afford a most agreeable entertainment".[21]

An instrument which was less versatile but equally interesting was the rock harmonican. This was exhibited in the academy of arts at Newcastle being he believed the second of its kind. It consisted of "4½ octaves with semitones formed of rude and shapeless blocks or slabs of Granwacke slate from Skiddaw. The largest is about 30 inches long, 4 inches wide and 2 inches thick. The smallest is about the size of one's hand. These are played upon with small hammers made of wood by three men and the effect is loud, clear and brilliant – the melody is of a novel kind and the tones are most harmonious".[21] He took his wife Jane and several friends during the week following his first sighting to see this unusual instrument.

On a journey to Wales in the company of his friend Dr Buckland in 1841 harp-players were to be found in several inns which the two travellers visited. This cheered them out of the rain at Llangollen and at Corwen in the half-flooded hall; but the poor man at Llanwrst performed his art in a passage or hallway so swimming with water that he was truly "drowned out". With thoughts of the ballad of Bedd Gelert known since childhood foremost in his mind, Sopwith particularly enjoyed the performance of the young harper in the comfortable hotel at the village of the same name. The lad was only 16 years old, well dressed and handsome as he played "The lass of Gowrie" and many other tunes, some accompanied vocally by the landlord. The ballad was a form included in evening entertainment with merry delight and Sopwith himself gave a rendering of "Canny Newcassel" on several occasions. This and the playing of the organ and piano by ear was the limit of his own musicianship. Piano lessons proved to be a waste of time and he reluctantly gave them up, resolved instead that his daughter Ursula should learn the violin after one particularly pleasant evening with the Probyns of Cheltenham.

* * *

It would be tedious to record every occasion of an evening's entertainment enjoyed by Sopwith even for one year. The breadth of entertainment open to a keenly alert mind might range from the enlargement of serious scientific knowledge to amusing anecdotes with friends, from visits to the opera and theatre to party fun at Christmas or the New Year. Zoos, botanical gardens, panoramas and dioramas seem to have been preferred to fairs or races, but

Aug. 26. 1843

116

Italian Opera house in London, viz. in the centre of the stage in front of the orchestra & raised above the level of the stage so as to form a desk for the leader of the band he had a frock on and appeared like an English waggoner in his working dress. —

The boxes have chairs placed in them in which arrangement more room as well as comfort is allotted than in the boxes of many English theatres which have contin ued seats. — The chairs are of birch, strong coarsely made, clumsy and heavy and but

Prompter in a Theatre.

there was no clear definition between the serious and the frivolous. There was an appetite for both.

The theatre was something of a highlight on his first London visit. Reference has already been made to Edmund Kean's dramatic appeal in the chaos following Act 4 of *Henry V* at Drury Lane. The music that followed, *Der Freischutz*, was fine enough but it was the scenery and effects that caught his imagination. "The scene of the incantation was gradually wrought up to a most horrible hideous and truly appalling spectacle – A large owl flapping his wings – green dragons and ill-omined (sic) birds hovering in the air with fiery serpents, green lights etc. moving in all directions – fiends with burning faces – skeletons and a livid picture of Pandemonium with a falling shower of fire and demoniacal screams completed the horrid climax".[23] Typically he goes on to describe the plan and aspect of the theatre in matter-of-fact detail, picking out the galleries, the gilt ribs of the ceiling, the chandelier and details of the decoration which are duly sketched. He computed that the theatre might hold 2,520 people and the orchestra had 36 members. Despite all this he enjoyed even more a good evening by the fireside amongst his possessions and papers.[*]

A special mention is made of a visit to Exeter Hall on April 25th 1837 when with his friends Fenwick and Donkin he heard Haydn's *Creation*. One of his favourites despite the lack of the solid grandeur to be found in Handel choruses, he particularly liked the first part: "Through all the Lands", "The Heavens are telling", "A new Created World" and "With verdure clad" were all admirable pieces of music. Clara Novello sang the last named before an intended tour to Italy and encores were demanded "by holding up and rustling the leaves of the books of the performance".[24] Another concert described at some length was Ole Bull's at the King's Theatre. Apart from Ole Bull's own violin playing there was

---

[*]   See chapter 8

Madame Pasta, Mademoiselles Blasis and Ostergard, several Italian singers, the principal cellist to the king of the French and a young harper called Taylor who was only 9 years old. Miss Cooper's rendering of "She never told her love" stirred the hearer deeply and Master Taylor's "Kathleen o' More" on the harp was admired for its sweetness and simplicity. A similar evening at Hanover Square rooms organised and led by Cipriani Potter gave him a further opportunity to hear Ole Bull and compare him favourably with Paganini. Despite what the critics had to say he also enjoyed a Tableau Vivant at Drury Lane where white figures in tight-fitting dresses portrayed *The Judgement of Paris*. McCready's Wolsey disappointed him at Covent Garden and the first taste of Italian opera in 1840 (Persiani's *Amina*) along with the ballet *Le Tarentule* elicits a stated preference for church music.

Visits to zoos or botanical gardens were a favourite occupation. In June 1837 there was a delightful if showery afternoon at the "Horticultural Society's gardens at Chiswick or Kew". Here there was an exhibition of fruits and flowers, a galaxy of fashion and three bands playing. Back in Newcastle he bought a share in the theatre for £29 so that he could spend an hour or two there from time to time, hardly allowing himself a whole evening. With Sir William Jackson Hooker and John Hancock he discussed the possible site for a botanical garden in Jesmond Dene, near the grounds of Armorer Donkin and Dr Headlam. A meeting under Mr. Buddle's chairmanship followed in August 1837. There was participation too in the Fine Arts Society alongside the Natural History Society, and with John Clayton he continued the search for a site for botanical gardens in Elswick fields. He kept his hand in at the organ in a veritable feast of opportunities in November 1837 when in London again. Mr. Davison of Hill and Davison accompanied him to the largest organ in London, at Christ Church, Newgate Street. From there they went to the new organ at Christ's Hospital, had an interlude at the United Services Museum, and then on to

Whitehall but they found the organ unworthy of the place. The new instrument, built by Hill and Davison for £1000 at the Chapel Royal, St. James was a great treat. Mr. Davison helped at the bellows while Sopwith enjoyed nearly 1½ hours playing, including patriotic pieces in the form of 'Rule Britannia' and the national anthem.

Ryan's new circus was an opportunity to be enjoyed at Birmingham when he was delayed from travelling on to Preston in February 1839. He recalls that Timour the Tartar was followed by clever horsemanship and rapid riding in the ring. A boy balanced on his head, high up on a pole; another vaulted "about 20 summersets in succession . . . Jem Crow was performed by the American actor Rice who has been so popular in London – the song was encored three times by a noisy and senseless gallery",[25] but he was disgusted at this depraved taste and came away early. More to Sopwith's liking on his coach journeys was reading: *Nicholas Nickleby* (the thirteenth instalment) was bought for his Mail journey to Exeter on April 2 1839, along with William Ellery Channing's *Self-Culture*.

Homely entertainment gains some place in the diary as the children grow and begin to ask questions. A late morning walk at Tynemouth in May 1839 with his wife Jane, the eldest son Jacob and their own eldest Ursula was a delightful relaxation by a beautiful sea. Later their father took Jacob and Ursula along Cullercoats Sands to Tynemouth priory where they were shown a coal seam and enjoyed the flowing tide. Jacob was asked what the sand was made of. "They are great rocks dashed all to pieces" was the reply and he was soon telling his sister that Jupiter "was much larger than this earth and contained millions of people". Father was pleased at their intelligence and "tolerable notions of many subjects of general information".[26] A large family picnic with the Burnups and Hindhaughs was another pleasure. Numbering eighteen in three carriages they went to Gosforth where they had "fruit, wine champaigne and a pleasant walk in the grounds" followed by tea and other refreshments in the Gardener's house, not returning until 9 p.m. on a pleasant August evening.[27]

The New Year of 1842 gives us a good a picture of adult and infant enjoyment in winter time. A dinner party at his sister's numbering ten, including all the children, six of his from Jacob to Emily, only a few weeks old, would appear to have been a midday meal. He was again at his sister's on his birthday, January 3rd, after attending a Joiners' Company meeting. A Mr. Heath at a large old house in the Bigg Market provided old-fashioned party fun on January 5th. There was a magic lanthorn and Sopwith accompanied various scenes with appropriate tunes on a large grand piano. A fire cloud followed and after this excitement older children and grown ups joined in a supper. After it "The Family Coach" was played: the players formed a huge circle and were denominated as the staff of the coach or its occupants, the whip, the door, Aunt Dorothy or the dear little dog. An excursion is taken to view the falls of Niagara, the names occurring frequently in the story read out. As each is named, the holder of the name gets up, turns round and sits down again. But if "The Family Coach" is mentioned, everyone gets up and changes places across the room. "Magic Music" ensued during which an actor comes in to perform a part, the only clue being given by the music, loud when the audience is "warmer" at guessing and quieter when "cooler". The evening finished with French Blind Man's Buff.

There were many other occasions when entertainment is mentioned, in the theatre, concert hall and at home. He did go to the races in 1843 shortly after Richard Clayton's sermon against them, watching them through a telescope from the grandstand having received a ticket for the week from Mr. Loftus: he also played quoits with cousin John at the workshop. Not averse to old customs he deplored those which might lead to excess of drink or any cruelty. Hiring fairs were apt to be occasions of the former, amusingly rustic but fraught with dissipation and im-providence, as at Haltwhistle in May 1840. Two final reflections might be made: the first is heavy if practical, the second more endearing.

A journey by coach from Preston to Carlisle was the occasion of a thorough perusal of *Amusements in retirement or the influence of Science, Literature and the Liberal Arts on the manners and happiness of private life.* He noted with approval the author's "two ages required by all of us: one to gain experience and another to profit by it. For men too frequently lose the principle portion of their existence in vain pursuits and idle speculations before they acquire the power of duly estimating the value of security, innocence and content". The question was how to mix pleasantry and gravity without descending into folly. A taste for the elegant and the beautiful could appreciate solitude which would not be boring but "a sphere for continual mental activity and the asylum of health, quiet and innocence". So silence can become "golden moments, a meditation on past labours or the maturing of designs for future excellence. The union of a cultivated imagination and an uncorrupted heart form a full and perfect diapason." The further requirements for happiness would be the "selection and estimation of a virtuous woman; experience enough to feel the value of a moderate fortune, and a taste to prefer the simple enjoyments of life to those more costly and more fatal pleasures which debase the mind, corrupt the heart and enervate the body".[28] Such temperance of view was admittedly written a few days after his return home to quietness and comforts with his dear Jane and the latest arrival, Anna. Perhaps he was using the words of another to congratulate himself on his own moderation. Always discreet, we only know that he enjoyed female company whether intellectual or not, especially that of Mrs Probyn at Longhope. Equally we know that Jane detested social bustle and ailed in the city life which was so different from her remote childhood at Ross, almost an island off the Northumbrian coast.

The more attractive preference with which to close the chapter is to be found at the fireside of Mr. Wood at Singleton Lodge,

Manchester. It led Sopwith to laud the quiet home and the society of occasional friends rather than the endless visiting and large parties. "The dull monotony of cards . . . and the stupidity of un-meaning conversation which frequently consume four or five precious hours in a large and promiscuous evening party" was anathema to one who liked select dinner parties, a charming drawing-room, "the absence of ceremony and the cheerfulness and intelligence and desire to please which happily prevails in many of the happiest 'homes of England'".[29]

Chapter 11

Dean Forest Commissioner

January 3rd 1833 was an important day for Thomas Sopwith. It was his thirtieth birthday and he could already look back with some degree of pride upon his work as surveyor and mining specialist. Apprenticeship as a mineral surveyor on the Greenwich Hospital Estates at Alston had led to the drawing of plans, levels and sections. Learning to engrave such drawings persuaded him further of their value to practising surveyors and company directors who might otherwise remain ignorant of past workings and potential value. Such drawings were equally valuable to the geologist. Industrialisation meanwhile provoked the need for better transport. The country of England itself should be crossed by canal or railway: Thomas Telford's overfull professional commitment was the opportunity for others like Sopwith to be engaged on the line from Corbridge to Haydon Bridge. The Otterburn road and the new Derwent road had also improved Newcastle's links north-westward and south-westward. Yet the year 1829 with its domestic tragedies* and the consequent increased responsibility in the cabinet making business had caused Sopwith to pause in his commitment to railway surveys, to pause and remain local in his horizons. So the offer received on January 3rd 1833 immediately enlarged his vision once more. For it was on that day that Mr. John Buddle arrived with an official letter.

The letter referred to a proposed survey of the mines in the royal Forest of Dean: the offer was from Mr. Alexander Milne of the

---

* His wife Mary died on July 28th. His father Jacob died on October 20th.

Woods and Forests Office in London. Thomas Sopwith was offered the job of surveyor, joining John Buddle of Wallsend and John Probyn of Cheltenham in this important task which would give him a truly national opening and, in the event, reputation from which an international career might have stemmed. No original diary entry does justice to the taking up of the new job but Sopwith set out, a seasoned traveller now, to enjoy the first of many journeys south to Gloucestershire in February 1833. With his characteristic pleasure in travel he found much to observe both of the landscape and the principal towns on his route.* The four day journey brought him at length to Coleford, the last part in the dark so that he was only vaguely aware of steep and woody hills with a few scattered fires marking the collieries.

His first acquaintance with the ancient Forest of Dean drew forth inevitable comparisons and a historical note. England itself had been well-wooded but now there were treeless wastes still bearing the name of forest such as Gilderdale near Alston. He recalled that Philip of Spain had set out to destroy the oaks of Dean Forest, a special objective of his great enterprise, the Armada, in 1588. Only recently had the government of Britain sought to re-plant and revive the forest. In this forest, the diarist records, there were several seams or veins of coal which emerged conveniently on opposite sides of the district. This enabled recovery of coal from the surface as well as through shafts into deep workings. The mineral wealth was not however given wholly to the crown. There were instead free miners who obtained gales from the agent of the crown known as the gaveller. These gale rights had caused much dispute, the more so because they could also be sold to "foreigners" some of whom invested considerable capital in the collieries. One such form of engrossment of gales was held by a proprietor whose collieries produced nearly half of the coal then raised in the forest. The proprietor was Edward Protheroe of Cheltenham.

---

*   See chapter 7

Edward Protheroe had seen the potential of the coal resources of the forest in the industrialisation of the north bank of the Severn estuary, with ready access to the metal industries of South Wales. The better known names of Crawshay and Guest also occur but it was Protheroe who had made steady acquisitions and plans through the 1820s, provoking anxiety amongst the free miners and regrets amongst some who had permitted inherited gales to be lost in their generation. In 1824 Protheroe established himself as "assignee of a term of 500 years from 24 August" and also became a "lessee for 42 years from 29 September 1831 under Thomas and John Morse, free miners".[1] In 1827 he had laid out 1500 yards of railway to join the Royal Pit to the Severn and Wye Railway. In 1829 he erected a steam engine and continued a railway line to join the Bullo Pill Railway.[2] Similar developments may have contributed to the confusion indicated by a memorial of 1825 "signed by 62 free miners and 14 other occupiers and proprietors . . . to the Gavellers, begging them not to gale any waterpit or waterwheel or engine within at least 1000 yards of the head of another free miner's".[3] Whether or not Protheroe had overstepped the mark in his developments he was initially most uncooperative towards the crown survey.

After commenting on the useful work by Dr Buckland and David Mushet whose plans formed the basis for his own detailed report, Sopwith observed of Protheroe that "this gentleman opposed so strong an objection to the survey being made that it led to the abandonment of the proposed survey".[4] It appears that John Buddle had caused offence, according to Protheroe, by seeking to enter a mine without first asking Protheroe for permission. Sopwith had applied to Edward Machin, king's gaveller or agent, of Whitemead Park but found him out. He then went to Park End Colliery where a Mr. Gething refused to let him "descend by Mr. Machin's engines without his express sanction". Gething had already been blamed for letting Mr. Buddle go down the mine. If the work had Mr. Protheroe's approval then Gething, as agent, would give every aid to the survey. Sopwith had to be content with viewing the district

during the next two days accompanied by a Mr. Hosmer, a surveyor, on one day and by Mr. Mushet, "a gentleman of great
scientific attainments", on the other. He did catch Mr. Machin
briefly on Friday 15th February but had to wait until Monday 18th
February for an interview at Whitemead Park. Here he was shown
Protheroe's letter about Buddle's mistake and which went on to say
"if any gentlemen should again think of making the descent I would
advise him to settle his worldly affairs first, as he would be very
unlikely to visit the surface of the earth again, unless he could find
his way without the aid of my machinery".[5]

Such an obstruction was naturally disturbing and greater authority was clearly needed. Sopwith wrote in detail to Buddle about the
survey and showed the letter to Machin who, as one of five
commissioners who had initiated the study, would be a valuable
ally. It was necessary then to send back the three subsurveyors to
Newcastle, go to London to await Buddle's reaction and, if summoned, explain himself "to the official agents of government
whose commission I was thus under the necessity of abandoning"[6].
It was not without wry humour that Sopwith noticed an election
squib, as he called it, in Bristol where he paused on his journey to
London. In the ruins of one side of Queen's Square, suffering from
the effects of the "tendency of democratic power", he saw written
on a wall in large letters:-

'WHO BURNT THIS? PROTHERO'

This Protheroe was the son of the man who had discomfited
Sopwith, but despite reflecting on the difficulties in Dean Forest
and on the burning of Bristol he did not allow this to spoil his visit
to the city nor his short stay at Bath. It is not revealed by Sopwith
how the matter of Protheroe's obstruction was resolved. He was in
London until early March, staying on after Dean Forest business to
attend a committee of the House of Commons on the Derwent
Road. The next references to the Forest of Dean find him pressing

A Levelling Party.

on with the survey most satisfactorily in March 1834, a survey which had resumed in December 1833, aided by 3 assistants.

The description given in his diary of the Forest of Dean unfolds gradually during the years of his involvement on business there. The romantic scenery in parts of it stands in contrast to the "wild and sterile" parts noted on his first visit at the points "where the numerous quarries and rugged outline of the narrow valleys" gave a more severe aspect.[7] Where the rocks were inclined he saw picturesque combinations. The coal workings were comprised in 3 districts, namely Bilston, Park End and Coleford High Delf districts. The main collieries in the two former districts were in the hands of Protheroe; those of the Coleford High Delf depended on a seam which lay under ninety-five yards of sandstone. This permeable rock made conditions in the wet seasons difficult and work would often have to stop for two days or more. In the summer the sandstone tended to act as a sponge. Not surprisingly he chose to leave the subterranean survey of that area until it was drier.

If human and physical obstruction caused delays below ground, there was a further reason for interruption on the surface. Despite the useful work of David Mushet there simply was no accurate surface map and none on a scale needed to record existing features, natural or man-made. Although pleasantly disposed towards Mr. Hosmer, Sopwith described that intelligent gentleman's work as tedious. Nor was it directly useful to a mining survey. It consisted of an extensive survey of the small enclosures of the forest. The spirit of reform certainly seems to have been in the air but if a proper assessment was to be made, more thorough and more accurate methods were needed. Even with three assistants and at times double that number, much of the surveying might be inaccurate unless more reliable equipment was used. It was this determination to produce accurate plans and sections, already seen in Sopwith's work on the lead mines of the Alston district, which led him to devise a staff of his own, described in a previous chapter.* With the advantages of his new staff, or stave, great progress could be made, improving on the work of W. Todd[8] and on his own sketching of the strata from information given by David Mushet.[9]

By 1835 mapping of the Forest of Dean was complete. There were 16 sheets of the area and an index map showing enclosures, collieries and railways.[10] Another coloured version of the index map shows the colliery areas, round the edges of the basin which lies in a north-east to south-west oval shape east of Coleford, from Ruardean in the north to Bream and Yorkley Bank in the South. Useful though this surface representation was, Sopwith had enough knowledge of the greater usefulness of geological models to recommend and use a three-dimensional model of the area. This was constructed about 1837 and could be dismantled to reveal the main coal seams and collieries, whether excavated by inclined passages (the slope method) or by shafts piercing the sandstone above, and then galleries within the slope or drift.† With the survey very largely completed, why did he go to the further expense of constructing a three-dimensional model? Was it for his own satisfaction of completing a job and improving on the recording of information in the survey?

A clue to the timing of the large Dean Forest model can be found in a meeting on Friday 14th April 1837. There had been some surprise and much gratification at the speedy dispatch with which the survey of the forest had been completed – gratification on the part of the Office of Woods and Forests, but no surprise on the part of the two Newcastle men, Buddle and Sopwith. They were accustomed to accomplishing what they set out to do so long as politics permitted. Patience might not always be Sopwith's forte, and certainly not with the local politics of Tyneside itself ‡ But the dispatch had been recognised at the highest level. Viscount Duncannon himself, First

---

*   See chapter 4
†   On the subject of Sopwith's maps and models, see ch. 14.
‡   See above chapter 6

Commissioner of Woods and Forests, had been highly satisfied, Milne told the surveyor in "a long, confidential and very gratifying conversation on the 14th April". Milne went on to outline the Board's intention and proposed arrangements. These are not specified in the diary but the drift is clear for the words "as Commissioner for Crown", indicating an extension of his work, appear in parenthesis. On the same day Sopwith attended in the Brighton Committee Room where railway business was being carried out at the reputed cost of five guineas a minute. Life at the hub of technological change was profitable.

It seems unlikely that the Dean Forest model was created entirely for the possibility that it might provide its maker with further preferment in his career. Yet it would have helped confirm, not just to engineers and surveyors, but even more widely to politicians and power-brokers in government, that competence in one major task for the crown might properly be rewarded or recognised in other ways. It was therefore with added delight that Sopwith learned, if he did not already know, that recommendation to the post of commissioner to the Forest of Dean, carrying out the requirements of an act of parliament soon to be passed in 1838, had been made by no less a geologist and influential academic than William Buckland.[12]

Dr. Buckland, Fellow of Christ Church, Oxford and later Dean of Westminster, distinguished geologist, had already been instrumental in furthering Sopwith's interests. In 1828 Buckland had been the recipient of six copies of geological and mining plans of Hudgill and Holyfield. He may have received a broadsheet or letter commending them from Walter Calverley Trevelyan[13] or heard of them from John Taylor or John Phillips, both of the Geological Society. He ordered copies of these plans and in June 1835 had been one of Sopwith's sponsors for membership of the Geological Society. Now in 1837 he invited Sopwith to the inner circle of the Geological Club, of which more later. Buckland had been approached "to recommend someone as a proper person to undertake the office of Mining Commissioner on the part of the Free Miners. "'I told them'", said the Doctor, "'that they must have nothing short of Newcastle and I named Mr. Buddle and yourself'".[14]

The wording of this diary entry is interesting. It implies that Sopwith was to act for the free miners, or at least that he saw himself so doing. A later, official record makes it clear that under the 1838 Act he was the Crown Commissioner to act on behalf of the board: John Probyn was to act on behalf of the Free Miners and John Buddle was to be the umpire. If there was any danger that the former members of the enquiry would collude to the advantage of one party or another, for the crown or for the miners, now that they formed the commission for hearing cases arising under the new Act, it does not seem to have arisen. A respect for the findings which emerged in the statute was not diminished and could still be found as late as the 1970s.[*] Disputes there were but the accuracy of the new survey could not be seriously questioned.

Who were the free miners whose activities were so vigorously reviewed and recorded? A great deal had been written about them and the Commissioners added their own findings in the report. Iron had been mined in Saxon times and the Forest was already royal property soon after the Norman Conquest. All males aged twenty-one in the hundred of St. Briavels could apply to be free miners. The delightful miner's brass in St. Briavel's church is a 14th century representation of the breed, equipped with pick, hod and candle-stick, this last held in his mouth, ready to be set alongside him in the gas-free workings, piercing the wall of the cavity where he could win his coal or ore. Younger boys also worked to help in the gales or concessions granted by the gaveller, assistants to the vern (partnership) which divided up the dole (share). Other land-owners might have a share by putting in a Lord's man alongside these King's men. Minutes of a meeting in 1675 could ask, "Have

---

[*] When I visited Vallets Level in 1973 enquiry from practising free miners about the 1838 report elicited the rejoinder "The Sopwith report? We still use it. It's our Bible for finding our way about the ground".

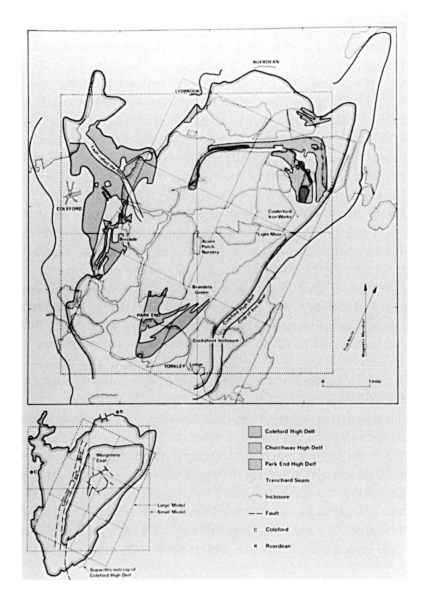

Index Map of the Forest of Dean.

there not always been . . . certain persons called and accompted free miners there; who have enjoyed . . . the liberty of entering, digging and working in the mines of coal and iron ore to their own proper use, and have they not always been called the King's miners?"

The freedom of the free miners was being challenged as we have seen, although not necessarily only by the bigger entrepreneurs such as Guest, Crawshay and Protheroe. The problems arose from increased activity to mine coal and ore, meeting the ready markets which arose in the revolutionary industrial period since Abraham Darby's discoveries. Darby's work in Coalbrookdale together with Newcomen's steam technology had led on to the famous Ironbridge by Darby's grandson and to a high-pressure boiler for Richard Trevithick's railway locomotive. There were therefore industrial and entrepreneurial pressures: equally there were simply physical pressures as workings crowded in upon one another. This is suggested by the memorial of 1825* to prevent encroachment by one set of workings upon others. The 1000 yard protection limit had been accepted in theory in 1754 and free miners had not been allowed to set up engines. The miners also faced a limit of a twelve foot radius from a water-pit. The ability to extract coal from the second (middle) series and the third (lowest series) was vital if the better quality coal was to be won. From the deeper levels coal and ore could be brought out by engines with winding gear. These workings could supplement and improve upon those which had the optimistic names of Ready Penny, Fair Play and Strip and At It, or encourage the labourers at the Perseverance workings. But the efforts of all these free miners required protection against the big men. Otherwise some might find only the implied miseries of Work or Hang Pit rather than the apparent good fortune of Lucks All gale.

The year of 1838 was an exceptionally busy one for Sopwith: Dean Forest affairs did not predominate until the autumn. He did not trouble to wait up to see the year in and although the servants

---

* See above, p. 127

were up at 4 a.m. expecting a belated first foot visit, it was 8 a.m. before the faithful George Muras knocked at the door with a bottle of whisky and a fruit cake. George had worked for the Sopwith joinery for nearly forty years and doubtless received a warm welcome. Thomas got on with his accounts that month of January and was soon involved in local improvements, seeing the new wood bridge for the Newcastle and Carlisle railway at Scotswood before surveying the old farm house at Dalavil. There were local opportunities for hearing and giving learned papers, plans to rebuild the joinery in Sandyford road on the northern edge of Newcastle town and plans to extend the Derwent road which involved a ride on horseback to Shotley Bridge and across to Stanhope. There were the preparations for the British Association meeting in Newcastle and the mobilisation of interest and support for his own projects. The successful meetings, referred to below (ch 12), were followed by a visit to Ireland in early November and an extensive review of the whole year closes a fruitful and busy time, recorded in the pages of no less than five diaries. It was in September and October that he took up responsibilities in the Forest of Dean having received a print of the Bill on May 4th.

The first meetings of the Dean Forest Commissioners show Sopwith very much in charge, even allowing for the fact that his diary and the minutes kept by him emphasise his direction of affairs. Both accounts record that the first meeting was in the King's Head Inn at Coleford on September 5th. It was too crowded for the number who turned up so the meeting adjourned to the Angel Inn where there was "a very spacious room. Having taken the chair I addressed the meeting on the nature and objects of the Commission and read the notes which I had written at Birmingham". In fact the first business recorded in the minutes was a declaration by the commissioners that they had no right, title, nor interest, a deposition which was signed by Edward Machin, magistrate and deputy gaveller.[16] As yet only Sopwith and Probyn were present. Preliminary arrangements for a tabular form on which to make claims were outlined and the diary states that Mr. Protheroe, Mr. Clark and others made some remarks and enquiries.

So too, but by letter, did the Jenkins brothers. On Saturday September 8th, between the first meeting and the agreement to meet next at the Speech House on Monday 10th, "a letter was received from John Jenkins and George Jenkins stating that Mr. Protheroe had taken from them by arbitrary power three gales called Freeminers' Right, Shadingtuft Water Works and Freeminers' Folly No 3". Other claims and disputes had already been received but Sopwith spent a relatively quiet weekend at the King's Head Inn. He had a cold which he blamed on the unseasonable weather so he stayed indoors after attending Coleford Chapel in the morning. The concentrated work rather than the 300 mile journey recently accomplished was probably catching up on him. He noted with approval that the *Monmouth Beacon* contained a long report of the first meeting but he does not state whether he had given a form of press release. The proceedings of the first meeting, it was stated in the report, "appeared to give great satisfaction".[18]

A full meeting of gentlemen, solicitors and free miners duly took place. Sopwith left for it in a chaise at 10 o'clock to travel the three miles from Coleford to the Speech House "in the very midst of the Royal Forest of Dean".[19] In his diary he refuses to outline the minutes again, as so often such details were committed to other professional notebooks. He explained the tabular claim form he had devised and the intention of the Commissioners to hear claims at the Bear Inn, Newnham, the Speech House and at the Feathers Inn, Lydney. He was beginning to warm to his task and greatly enjoyed venturing out to discover more of the forest scenery: the solid Speech House itself with its discomforts accorded well with its purpose as courthouse for the ancient mine laws, set as it was amongst large, stately oaks. A further meeting on Tuesday, letter-writing and business at the King's Head on Wednesday, including correspondence with Sir John Robison about barometer tubes and Sir Charles Lemon about the School of Mines in Cornwall, were interspersed with a visit to Wynd Cliff, a steep precipice above the Wye, and a limestone cavern. Here a Welsh harper was playing the double harp, being a silver medallist from some earlier competition, one of four prizes he had won. What a romantic introduction to a longed-for visit to Tintern now at last visited and described at length. He did not have time to sketch it but he hoped that the architect Charles Barry would study it if he came on a geological tour with de la Beche and Dr William Smith of Scarborough.

There were fewer free miners at the court meeting in the Speech House on Thursday September 13. Protheroe and a number of solicitors were there. The main subject of discussion was the Tormentor Pit, aptly named according to Sopwith's diary, and proceedings were adjourned until September 17th at Newnham. Visits to Archdeacon Probyn at Longhope Manor and to John Probyn's house at Cheltenham were even more enjoyable because of an opportunity to hear music in the Cathedral at Gloucester. The only slight snag to orderly progress and preparation was lack of light on the morning of September 16th. Waking at 4 a.m. Sopwith found that he had left his pens, and the vestas with which to light the candles, in the drawing room. He began to grope his way out of his room but a small lap dog called Fury appeared. Rather than let Fury's barking wake everybody else, he gave up the idea of recovering pens and matches and wrote in the dark for an hour. At 6 a.m. he set out for a good walk, followed by a ride and a bath at the Montpelier baths before 8 o'clock breakfast with the Probyns. Later there was church, dinner at 3 p.m., a walk with the whole Probyn family and a pleasant musical evening after tea.

Further evidence was being collected over the next few days, some heard at the Speech House, some at Newnham and some at the mines themselves. The diary says little about these occasions but rather more about visits to the Machins at Whitemead Park or the Probyns in Cheltenham, as well as to a dinner at the Jones household of Hay Hill, presided over by the Reverend Mr. Jones, "one of the old school – a hearty and hospitable parson".[20] At

Coleford.

Whitemead he was able to show off the model of Dean Forest to a party of some twenty ladies, gentry and clergy and later in the day was delighted to receive from the carpenter a travelling desk which he had designed. This would appear to be a different example from that mentioned earlier (ch. 4), being altogether larger and deeper in its accommodation of books, papers and instruments.

The desk would certainly be useful. Sopwith frequently rose at 5 a.m. and worked for three or four hours on the Mine Law Courts orders, on minutes of meetings or on regular business elsewhere. Letters to Charles Barry, the architect, or James Rendel, the engineer, shared the ideas of the busy improvers of England, keeping his interests and name before them at an ever more successful period of his career. The Orders of the Mine Law Courts were read in digest on October 2nd when a Court was held at the Angel Inn under Buddle's chairmanship. Buddle had arrived the previous day and reviewed the proceedings so far with Sopwith. There was a complaint by a Mr. Baker against the Cheltenham company. Mr. Mushet called for information on forest customs and the memorial of 1825 was mentioned as well as an order of 1775. No other details occur in the diary and the meeting adjourned at 4 p.m. Observations continued on rides or walks through the forest and further business was carried out on October 4th. Hospitality was enjoyed at the home of General Dighton, "a stout, healthy and active veteran of 78, who after spending 40 years in the burning suns of India is now enjoying an honourable old age in the beautiful village of Newland".[21]

By October 10th the first series of meetings of the Commissioners of Dean Forest were over. What became of the complaint by the Jenkins brothers against Protheroe?[22] The diary does not recall the decision but the minute book of proceedings shows that the Jenkins had sold their gales to Protheroe.* Sir John Guest attended

---

*   George Jenkins, commonly called "Bull Jenkins", was sketched by Buddle during a sitting of the Dean Forest Commission - Diary No.25 p 149.

the second series of meetings to make statements about iron mines in the Westbury district. Sopwith renewed his friendship with Mrs Probyn, staying with old Archdeacon Probyn at Longhope. He particularly enjoyed a walk up May Hill, enjoying the view to Gloucester Cathedral, the Malverns and the Severn. While there is evidence of much writing and report-making, no further details are given.

The work proceeded smoothly enough and continued in the spring of 1839 when more than twenty claims were heard on April 16th. The meeting on April 30th "was long and very tedious . . . Mr. Protheroe and a great number of Owners of Mines, Claimants for Gales, Agents, Solicitors, Free Miners and Idlers were present".[23] The work in mid March 1840 was described as "the intricate and perplexing business of the Forest". A visit to Mr. Protheroe at Hill House in April to discuss the Mining rules and regulations and the proposed railway to Gloucester led to pleasanter discourse. Protheroe knew his man and showed Sopwith one of Mott & Co's "Patent Sostenenti grand" pianos on which Mrs Protheroe obligingly played a few tunes to elicit sounds resembling a seraphine, but softer. On June 29th 1840 a deputation of the principal mine owners expressed their thanks to the Commissioners in very complimentary terms. On March 8th 1841 a further landmark was reached in the signing of the Award of Coal Mines in the Forest of Dean. There were three copies, each containing 30 skins of parchment and 40 plans. 105 separate collieries were awarded: a major task had been completed.

With that work behind them, Buddle and Sopwith descended, on the same day, Mr. Jackson's Sling pit to see iron workings in the so-called Crease stone, an arenaceous limestone. Over the next few days other iron workings were seen near Cinderford Brook, at the Buckshaft pit, at the Shakemantle new pit and at Oakwood China Level. All this activity, together with the furnaces of Park End and the noise of the workmen's hammers contrasted strangely with the great silence and solitude of the forest. It had not lost its romantic grandeur in the months they had known it but the Forest of Dean was now more familiar and less daunting. The variety may best be finally summed up in the description of a journey towards Ross, riding in Mr. Probyn's phaeton on April 24th 1839. In ten miles they saw "the wild broken scenery of the forest, its wide open roads – its bare and cheerless 'meends' or common traversed with numerous roads and disfigured by shapeless heaps of waste from the coal mines – the rude machinery at the pits – the stately beeches and the vast and undulating surface of its Inclosures . . . the distant view comprehending the steep and woody banks of the Wye near Monmouth . . . the Buckstone hill . . . the hills of Brecon and Glamorgan".[25]

The Survey was done. Man's handiwork might spoil, but it had been observed, measured and assessed. The Forest of Dean might have a long history and hold out great opportunities, but its mysterious and romantic kaleidoscope could now be related to its geology as well as its haphazard history and custom. For the one to whom it had yielded more of its secrets there were new vistas and a new confidence to advance as geologist, scientist and surveyor.

Chapter 12

Geologist and Scientist

It is not the purpose of this chapter to set out the place of geology or the progress of science in the first half of the 19th century as reflected in the career of Thomas Sopwith F.G.S., F.R.S. Nevertheless he encountered many geologists and men of science, aspired to be one of their number and received sufficient contemporary recognition to deserve re-examination of his reputation today. No such re-examination can avoid the paradox of eager practical progress opposed by the strongholds of intellectual tradition. On the one hand the industrial revolution threw up a mass of experimentation: on the other hand the philosopher sought to construct a system of belief in the wake of political upheaval in the French Revolution and of its contemporary, the Romantic Age in Germany. If the latter sought some grand speculative, physical and spiritual synthesis of the whole world, its purpose seems at odds with the educational scene prevalent in England in the years after victory at Waterloo.

Education, if it was ever confined solely to classroom curriculum, would have a gloomy record in the early 19th century. Judging from histories of education the schools and universities of England were marked by a lethargy and conservatism which contrasts with the energy of industrialisation. But education arises from a much wider range of sources than the schoolroom. There are the philosopher-manufacturers such as Josiah Wedgwood with a huge influence in the founding of learned societies and patronage of science. There are the country parsons who maintained long debates through discourses in literary reviews and philosophical tracts, all the while studying the natural history of their surroundings or constructing better optical instruments to observe phenomena near and far. If the gentlemen-amateur continued long in Britain it should not be supposed that other classes or occupations were excluded from a growing number of institutions; some were in the literary and philosophical tradition but many discussed a wide variety of scientific subjects. The antiquarian interest which caught Thomas Sopwith's youthful imagination was only one of the many subjects which he took up. Architecture, astronomy and later meteorology all stemmed from the keen observation of a practical mathematician. But it was in the course of his initial major task away from the craftsman's bench in the cabinet works, as a minerals surveyor at Alston, that he first sought to pursue an abiding interest in geology.

The mining districts of Alston became the text-book, lecture-theatre and place of study for one who had received little formal schooling but much encouragement from an able mathematical teacher. We do not know how long Thomas was in Henry Atkinson's school but it is certain that he learned how to use a telescope and microscope, how to measure and draw accurately. As a minerals surveyor in the Alston district in the late 1820s he was soon applying his skills of accurate observation to produce mining plans and seeking to further the cause of geological records. These, he argued, were a matter of economy, efficiency and safety in the immediate vicinity of existing mine-workings. Learning from them, mine owners would be saved expense and extend their profitable exploitation of veins and seams. There was nothing more wasteful than speculative working without geological knowledge. Worst of all uncharted earlier workings were a constant threat where collapse and drowning out of new workings might occur. The lessons to be learned on the small-scale in one locality could be equally usefully applied across a region and ultimately across the kingdom. Later still the well-learned lessons would be applied in Europe, by Sopwith himself in Belgium and by his sons Thomas and Arthur in a more purely practical sense in Spain, Switzerland and India. The mining and civil engineering works which they developed were a practical outworking of geological studies. Sopwith's own mentor in a more systematic study of geology was the Reverent Robert Turner in about the year 1830.

Geology was in the early 19th century the leading science. Philosophically its study might lead to speculations on the age and history of the Earth although it was finding the order, and naming the strata, of rocks which predominated. Practically geology's use was the development of mineral and other natural resources. It is in the latter field that Sopwith can lay some claim to importance, encouraged and aided by Professor Buckland, and expressed partly through the Geological Society of London, partly through the meetings of the British Association for the Advancement of Science and frequently through informal meetings and correspondence with other geologists. It was through the portals of the Geological Society and the Geological Club that Sopwith passed to rub shoulders with the foremost geologists of the day. Their friendship brought him into a wider circle of scientists and this acquaintance, together with his abilities, propelled him to the highest courts of scientific discussion in the land. The origins of the Geological Society pre-dated his career, being founded in 1807, but the wisdom of Sir Charles Lyell and others which led to the establishment of the government's geological survey under de la Beche in 1835 was contemporaneous with Sopwith's most active period of geological interest. It was in 1835 that he was admitted to the Geological Society, sponsored by John Phillips and supported by Sedgwick, W.J. Hamilton, Murchison and Buckland. In December of the same year his Fellowship of the Institution was formally noted.

The Geological Society had survived an attempt by the Royal Society at amalgamation. This was in the days when Sir Joseph Banks ruled and believed that the Royal Society should be the only scientific society. Indeed the Royal Society had suffered much criticism from those who believed that it cast its net too widely to embrace those of little true scientific pretension let alone achievement. The masterful days of Banks were followed by less powerful leadership from Davies Gilbert and Humphry Davy and reform seemed even less likely under the royal Duke of Sussex. Medical men were prominent in showing their dislike of the lack of reform. Nevertheless there were changes in the 1820s, indicated by the changed wording of the certificates of membership. Literary and antiquarian interests were no longer the only criteria for entry: they were replaced by a devotion to "literature and natural knowledge, or science "or, in the case of those who were not practising scientists, "addiction to literature and science".[1] Still greater criticism was levelled at the Royal Society by a remarkable mathematician, Charles Babbage.

Babbage, the creator of a famous calculating machine, had personal reasons for attacking the Royal Society: he believed that he should have received a medal for his scientific prowess in 1826. It was perhaps largely because of the slow response of the Royal Society to change and his own grand desire to further the status of science that drove Babbage to help found the British Association in 1831. Yet even the confidence implied by the full title of this great venture – the British Association for the Advancement of Science – should not lead us to suppose that the term "scientist" was becoming more clearly defined. It has been suggested that Dr William Whewell coined the term for those who studied material nature; but the description might still stand awkwardly alongside the earlier belief by Coleridge that "the clerisy was a permanent, learned class or order, a sort of national church of intellectual instructors".[2] The meetings of the BAAS became grand and festive occasions not only for the gentry of science (and the reservations about ladies were challenged in theory by Mary Somerville and in practice by Pauline Jermyn, the seventeen year old bluestocking who became Mrs Walter Calverley Trevelyan) but also for the practising engineers. The British Association was indeed a great opportunity for Thomas Sopwith; but since that occasion did not occur until the BAAS came to his home town of Newcastle in 1838, and his part in it was at least as much assured as a geologist rather than as an engineer, it is more appropriate to consider his contribution to the Geological Society first of all.

It was on June 5th 1835 that Sopwith's association with the Geological Society was notified. Fellowship Certificate number 1070 shows that John Phillips was the main sponsor. Phillips was now professor of Geology at King's College, London and an assistant secretary of the BAAS since 1832. Election followed on November 18th and the acceptance of the fellowship with the fee of ten guineas was recorded on December 7th. The new fellow appears to have attended the annual dinner of the Society on February 19th 1836, but there is nothing beyond the one line entry in his diary to indicate participation in the affairs of the Society.

Why had Sopwith received membership of the Geological Society of London? His name was certainly becoming known outside the north-east of England, not only through railway surveys and mineral surveys: the latter included an important occasion of giving evidence on the matter of sulphur wells at Harrogate.[3] Availability for this case however probably arose from acquaintance already made with scientists, both in the Geological Society and on other occasions, notably acquaintance with Dr William Buckland to whose star Sopwith's geological reputation is to a large extent attached. The invitation by Thomas Telford to become a member of the Institute of Civil Engineers in 1833 marks that dual position as practising surveyor and engineer alongside the scientific interests that Sopwith had clearly shown from his earliest days. In the following year his 'Treatise on Isometrical drawing', dedicated to John Buddle who had suggested it, marked a new stage in his career. The practising surveyor on his most important national task to date, the survey of the Forest of Dean, sought to publish an expertise in mathematical drawing which had long interested him and which had already emerged in the Holyfield mining plans.*

It was in 1837 that Buckland's interest and introductions led to more direct involvement in the Geological Society. The happy accident of being in Oxford at the end of term amidst increased student traffic made it impossible for Sopwith to leave the city as early as he had intended. Buddle and Sopwith had called at Christ Church and left a note. As it was Sopwith had to decline a subsequent invitation to breakfast, but he did call at 9 a.m. on June 8th 1837.[4] He has left a description of Dr Buckland's house which impressed itself on him more than the name of a young lady left blank in the diary, whom he saw in the drawing-room. Here he met Dr Locke, Professor of Chemistry in Cincinnati. Whether breakfast was eaten or not, he met Mrs Buckland in the breakfast room, Dr Davies Gilbert, past president of the Royal Society, and Mr. Edward Bigge. Sopwith referred to Buckland's "present of the Bridgewater Treatise on Geology to which he said that he felt more indebted for information which he had received from us"†, that is from Buddle and Sopwith.[5] Here indeed was an important focus of geological study at the time, and Sopwith was receiving an acknowledged part in providing evidence. Better still, there was an invitation to dine at the Geological Club on June 13th.

The Geological Club consisted of the favoured few and their guests. It was not so much an inner society as the convivial meeting of several members who might invite others. These guests might include those who were to give papers, foreign visitors or just scientific friends. The diners would, after satisfying one appetite, resort to the Society in Somerset House and partake of scientific fare. It is to be hoped that those who had dined elsewhere enjoyed their evening too. If there were dislikes and petty jealousies or disputes over the matters discussed, Sopwith's diary remains discreet.

*   See chapter 3
†   One illustration, of a fossil tree at Cresswell, bears Sopwith's hand. See
     Bridgewater Treatise, 2nd Edition, 1837, plate 56

He was more concerned to be seen dining with the distinguished than entering the academic fray. The information he supplies may be useful but chiefly only as a record of who sat next to whom by means of a diagram. The first of such occasions which the diary records states that there were some 30 present. Dr Whewell, President of the Society, presided at the dinner and Mr. John Taylor was in the vice-chair. On Taylor's left sat Buddle, Murchison, Buckland, Sopwith and Hutton. Opposite Buckland sat Lord Cole, the future Earl of Enniskillen in whose estates Sopwith would soon be involved, and Sir R. Donkin. The dinner was excellent, the conversation intelligent and vivacious.[6] Arm in arm, Buckland and Sopwith went off to Somerset House. The doctor had an umbrella and a blue bag which Sopwith asked if he might carry. Buckland told him that the bag had been honoured by Lord Grenville carrying it and disgraced by being the object of disapproval. He had tried visiting Humphrey Davy but been turned away. This happened three or four times and Davy's servant assured his master that Buckland had not called, but only "a man with a bag . . . and I always told him you were out".[7]

The meeting on June 13th is one of the few on which information of any note is supplied. Sedgwick read a paper on coal formation in North Devon which is described as being "a party question of considerable moment".* An hour and a half's discussion followed. G.B. Greenough "decried the policy of making minute local distinctions in geology", speaking "somewhat warmly", probably because his geological map was under fire Sopwith supposed. De la Beche felt even more criticised since the more recent work of the Geological survey was impugned. Fitton, knowledgeable on the south eastern chalk districts, and Murchison tended to support Sedgwick. So did Sopwith. Sadly no other account of the Geological Club or Society from Sopwith's pen gives as much insight into the debates of the day.

* See the *Great Devonian Controversy* by Martin J.S. Rudwick.

The year 1838 was an immensely important one to Sopwith. The British Association made its way north and he played no small part in welcoming the gentlemen of science to his home town, furthering his own interests, displaying those of the region and carrying out a successful campaign upon the government. With such activity, continuing Dean Forest business, now that he was a Commissioner, and a visit to Ireland there really was not time to fit in further London visits. 1839 was different. Although he does not set out the places at table, Sopwith gives note of another distinguished academic gathering at which he was privileged to be present. He had been visiting South Wales to pursue professional work at Ebbw Vale and Sirhowy. On the journey from Cheltenham in the Berkeley Hunt coach he had enjoyed the four hour journey to Oxford reading the whole of Sedgwick's "Discourse on the Studies of the University". On reaching Oxford he hurried to the lecture room to hear the last lecture in Buckland's course on mineralogy, on saliferous and inflammable minerals. Buckland was in good fettle, surrounded by specimens and spicing the lecture with cheerful comment. He performed one of his experiments to close the lecture by applying a red hot poker to a piece of dysodile. He remarked that he sometimes found the resulting offensive smell useful for clearing the room of stupid people. The audience, both wise and foolish, left swiftly.

What would Sopwith have made of the next intellectual offering? Buckland, Conybeare and he heard John Keble on 'Poetry', delivered in Latin. Dinner brought more comfortable circumstances and subjects in a language he could understand, though not perhaps entirely. There was Shuttleworth, Warden of New College, theologian and paraphraser of the Pauline epistles; Cardwell, principle of St. Albans hall, numismatist; P.B. Duncan, fellow of New College and curator of the Ashmolean; Conybeare, who invited him to come to Axminster; T. Short, fellow of Trinity College; Edward Bigge, Fellow of Merton; Baden Powell, Professor of Geometry with whom he talked about his volume on isometrical drawing, a copy

of which Buckland obligingly put on the table for Baden Powell
and Conybeare to see; Dr. Daubeny, professor of Chemistry and
finally Dr. Winterbottom, physician. Various spouses are also
mentioned and later he met Mr. Ruskin in the drawing room. It was
clearly a most satisfactory evening and a pleasant forerunner to the
next Geological Club dinner.

On March 13th 1839 Buckland presided at the Club. There were
sixteen at dinner and Sopwith gives some notes concerning most
of them; Haliburton, American judge, author of Sam Slick's say-
ings and doings; Broderick, conchologist; Greenough, leading
geologist; Captain Pringle and Colonel Mudge of the Ordnance
Survey; Lord Northampton, President of the Royal Society; Sir
Philip Egerton, a zealous geologist; John Taylor, leading mining
engineer; Dr. Mantell "[whose] name is well known" and Mr.
Ferguson M.P. an "agreeable and talented gentleman", married to
Lady Elgin. He makes no special mention of Sir Charles Lemon of
Carclew on his right, nor of Lord Fitzalan, a nephew of the Duke
of Norfolk. The table plan also shows a Mr. Mantell and Mr.
Barclay. Dinner took two and a half hours, and was completed by
tea and coffee. Buckland introduced Sopwith to Lord Northampton
as the group set out for the meeting. Here they met Sedgwick, de
la Beche, Murchison, Phillips and others, not least Dr. William
Smith "father of geology", whom Sopwith was glad to see again.
Mr. Hamilton read a paper on the geology of part of Asia Minor
and Sopwith had a long conversation with de la Beche before going
with Buckland to Lord Cole's for supper – "we found a very jovial
and scientific party and stayed till near 2 o'clock". The party
included many of the names already mentioned as well as Mr. Clift,
curator of the College of Surgeons, Lieut.-Col. Colby, head of the
Ordnance Survey, and Major Clarke, who had "lost a leg at
Waterloo". Colby talked about the Ordnance Survey and mining
schools to Sopwith: George Rennie was another whom he met and
conversed with at length. "The whole party was very merry and on
leaving, Lord Cole invited me to breakfast with him on Friday

morning".[8] After 4 hours sleep at the most Sopwith was up at 6, writing till 8, breakfasting at 9 with Buckland and busy with Mr. John Walker and his maps of India by 10 before a visit to Sir Francis Chantrey and an important meeting of the Mining Records Committee. He was thriving on the pace of intellectual, convivial and professional pursuits.

Equally important to Sopwith as the Geological Society meetings themselves were the friendships made with geologists and notably map-makers. A short stay with Greenough on March 15th and 16th where he met Babbage, Robert Hutton M.P. for Dublin and Mr. Jukes (en route for a geological survey of Newfoundland) gave him four hours of study in his host's library. Down in Cornwall in April he stayed at Carclew, Sir Charles Lemon's beautiful house set in a much admired deer park. Riding over to Falmouth, Lemon and his guest met T.B. Jordan, instrument maker with meteorological interests, and Robert Were Fox, the Quaker Scientist who, with his daughters, did so much to bring the Cornwall Polytechnic to a wider public. Sopwith made his contribution in two forms, neither of them geological. The Misses Fox kept an autograph scrap book to which he obligingly added the wisdom of an Alston Moor miner. "If folk wad nobbit let folk like folk as weel as folk wad like to like folk, folk wad like folk as weel as folk ever liked folk since folk was folk". He added an original design for globes, terrestrial and celestial, and his own method of recording weather. The latter he also wrote up for Mr. Fox and it is recorded in the Report of the Royal Cornwall Polytechnic for 1838.

The further acquaintance with geologists and scientists ran parallel to Sopwith's reputation in the Institute of Civil Engineers. Not long after he had seen Babbage's calculating machine crunching out the cube of 18 in 13 seconds by moving a handle back and forth twice, he was at Mr. Bryan Donkin's talking about phrenology. Donkin, it was noted approvingly, had one of Sopwith's monocleid cabinets in his study. At 6.30 p.m. on March 19th 1839 the two of them went to the Institute of Civil Engineers in Great

George Street: Donkin attended the council meeting as a vice president while Sopwith talked to Mr. Rendel. A meeting followed at which Josiah Parkes spoke on steam boilers. The geologist Farey was there; Colonel Colby and his assistant Carrington both wanted to see the Dean Forest model. It was however not the model but the levelling-stave which received recognition in the Year Book of Facts in Science and Art in 1839.

Meanwhile an important academic opportunity arose for Sopwith in October 1839. He was invited to be an examiner of the Engineer Students at Durham University. He was escorted to the splendid rooms, reserved for the senior judge when on circuit, in the castle at Durham. He describes going to the library to get "the answers to the general questions"[9] and his visit was made pleasurable by services in the cathedral as well as dinner with Warden Thorp and the students. He took the papers off to work on them for four hours until midnight and two days later met with Mr. Temple Chevallier and Professor Johnston* "to decide on the relative merits of the students and finally arranged them in classes".[10] For this service he received ten guineas.

Two occasions in 1840 show the geological fraternity exercising its charms for Sopwith as he met new faces and received the plaudits of his fellows. With William Buckland as president he was given special opportunities of introduction to guests and of converse with the most important members of the Geological Club. At the first of the two occasions, on April 8th, he had a busy day at his Berners Street house with a brief sortie to the Office of Woods and Forests and to the solicitor of the board. At 6 p.m. Buckland led into dinner placing Major-General Sir Thomas Mitchell on his right, Sopwith next to him, and the conversation with the distinguished surveyor-general of Australia included a discussion of surveying, planning, engineering and modelling.[11] Buckland was

---

* The Revd. Temple Chevallier, Professor of Mathematics and Dr. J.F.W. Johnston, Lecturer in Chemistry and a keen supporter of the BAAS, see Dr. C. Preece *The Durham Engineer Student of 1838*.

delighted with the success of his dinner placing, Lord Northampton being on his left and joining in. At the subsequent meeting of the Society it was Buddle's turn to present a paper describing the curious fault in Dean Forest known as 'The Horse'. Buddle however was not present: Mr. Hamilton read it instead. The paper included several of Sopwith's plans. Captain Basil Hall's paper on the sea-bed round the wreck of the Royal George at Spithead followed. After three other papers, Buckland returned to discussing Buddle's paper and gave Sopwith the chance to explain his Dean Forest model, which was on view, in more detail.

The August meeting of the Geological Club which Sopwith attended at Buckland's invitation at the Crown and Anchor was notable for different reasons. Sopwith was at the president's right hand: next to him was Captain Ibbetson and opposite were Featherstonhaugh, Sir Thomas Mitchell and Captain Basil Hall. The diary entry makes no further comment on the dinner but records that at the very moment of the meal an attempt was made on the life of Her Majesty and of Prince Albert. Edward Oxford fired two pistols. No bullets were found in the carriage however. Sopwith does not say how the news came but doubtless it spread like wildfire and instead of going to the Geological Society meeting, he went to the German Opera where he had a box opposite the royal box. The royal box was of course empty. He turned up at the Geological Society at 11 p.m. for tea and chat after the meeting and the following morning had a breakfast party which included Buckland, Mitchell and Dr Reid, the engineer engaged on ventilating the new Houses of Parliament.

About this time Clegg's atmospheric railway was a subject of interest to Sopwith. He met Clegg one day at breakfast and went along to see the half-mile of line and workings at Wormwood Scrubs, not expecting to see the machinery in action, but he had a ride on the train. He had high hopes of this ingenious method of locomotion working on the principal of vacuum: stationary steam engines pumped out air from a tube and the train was drawn along into the vacuum thereby caused. It was an idea taken up by Brunel but which failed because of the difficulty of maintaining sufficient vacuum. It is usually stated that the leather and grease of the sealing rings and flaps proved too attractive to hungry rats. Of other developments photogenic registration in these very early days of photography was another continuing interest while acquaintance was made with General Shrapnell and his gun, Hughes' pneumatic pumps, Garnett's two-armed telegraph and Armstrong's experiments with electricity in steam. Armstrong, W.D. Anderson and Sopwith were trying a number of experiments in this together at Seghill on October 21st 1840. Sopwith sent a memorandum to R.W. Fox and Armstrong drew up a statement which he sent to Faraday and which appeared in the *Philosophical Magazine* for December.[12]

In recording Sopwith's work as a geologist and scientist it is easy to be diverted into numerous lines of enquiry as he avidly sought to acquaint himself with experiment and improvement all round him. Here we see him engaged in original work with Armstrong, the Newcastle solicitor, who became one of the great entrepreneurs of the North and would allow Sopwith to be involved in his gunnery experiments in the wake of Crimean War failure, experiments which were demonstrated on the moors above Allenheads, Sopwith's home from 1846. It was there too that Faraday would pay a visit in 1856, and in 1863 savants from the British Association came for a soaking on excursion from the second meeting to be held in Newcastle. But to close the record of his achievement as a member of the Geological Society, the events of 1841 must be briefly sketched and reference made to other meetings from 1842 to 1845.

Over a basin of soup at the Salopian Inn in London, Sopwith renewed the friendship with Buckland on January 6th 1841. He showed Buckland a set of 30 models and was assured that they should be put on the table at the meeting that evening. They were to illustrate the paper which he had written on the journey south and was to deliver at the meeting. Dr. Fitton also called, comparing notes with cloth models he had devised for his geological study of the Hastings area. At the Geological club dinner in the Crown and Anchor the customary conviviality was enjoyed, Sopwith sitting at Buckland's left with Murchison and Lyell almost opposite. They adjourned as usual to the Society at 8.30 where the models had been laid out and Sopwith read his paper. It was followed by two others on Madeira and Aden respectively, given by Mr. Smith of Jordan Hill and Mr. Frederick Barr. Mr. Greenough rose to make observations saying that he had a series of models made to the designs of Mr. Farey which he thought had never received proper recognition from the Society. He would present them to the Society. At the same time he thought that they were less instructive than those which they had before them. Dr. Buckland was more flattering and also alluded to the Dean Forest model, considering that "the facile construction of such models as forming a new era in geological science "(Sopwith's words).[13] After a meeting at the Institute of Civil Engineers on January 12th, in which the question of mining records and models was prominent, there was a further visit to the Geological Club and Society on January 20th. Buckland placed Captain Basil Hall on his right and Sopwith next to Hall to "have some crack with him."[14] Horner and Greenough sat opposite: Lyell and Murchison were alongside. It was Sopwith's first meeting with Horner. At the Society Mr. Owen read a paper On the Sandstones of Warwickshire, their fossils and especially the "Labyrynthadon" (sic). Sopwith relished being party to the scene of "animated discussion . . . in which several of the most eminent English Geologists took a part and the acuteness, research and humour of their several addresses afforded a high intellectual treat".[15] Buckland had just received an exciting packet from Agassiz. He opened it and drew out '*Études Sur les Glaciers*' which Sopwith accepted gratefully.

The diary completes the account of the evening by admiring the assembled company yet again. Here was Sopwith's friend and mentor, Buckland, surrounded by the eminent geologists of the day; Owen, Sedgwick, Lyell, Murchison, Greenough and de la Beche. The last was challenged to explain what he meant by very great antiquity with reference to the age of the world. "If I am hard pressed on that point I should say that I consider these remains to be of very great antiquity as regards historical periods and of very little antiquity as regards geological periods", he replied. What company and what an evening to savour as the diarist returned to Berners Street.

The entry for the May 19th meeting is briefer. Professor Whewell was presiding: Buckland, Buddle, Sir Charles Lemon and Lyell were all dining. Sopwith sat at the left of the vice-president, John Taylor. The Society heard Buckland on hole-boring snails in limestone and J.S. Bowerbank on moss agates. This was also the occasion when Sopwith presented a set of twelve four inch models to the Society but no other comment occurs. Earlier in the year on a coach journey from Bristol to Farrington Gurney he had a geological conversation with a lady traveller. "I very often meet with persons in travelling who express much interest in Geology and infer from thence as well as from other indications that this science is rapidly gaining in popular estimation".[16] The entry for the November 3rd meeting is also brief. Greenough presided at the Club and Murchison at the Society, having returned from Russia only at the midnight before the meeting. Sedgwick read a paper on slate rocks and the carboniferous formation, "an animated and very amusing discussion" following.[17]

A Geological Club dinner which Sopwith again records by place-names in 1842 occurred on May 18th. He reflects as he often does on the distinguished company but goes to a lecture on Chemistry by Dr. Reid at Exeter Hall instead of attending the Society papers, only returning there at discussion time later on in the evening. In April he had already enjoyed Murchison's paper on the geology of Russia, admiring the beautiful drawings, maps and sections which accompanied the work of the President, and those

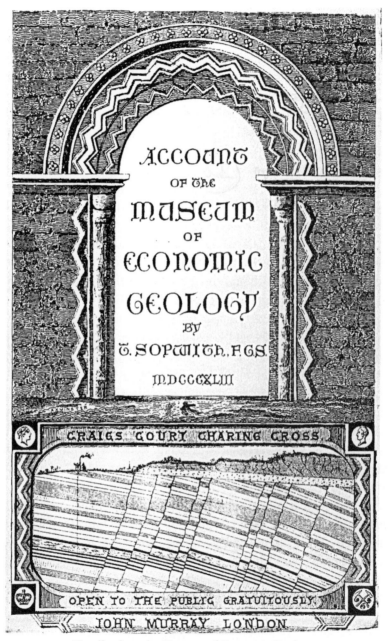

Handbook to the Museum of Economic Geology.

of Count Le Keyserling and M. de Vernieul: on May 5th he had the distinguished foreign geologists to breakfast to show them his geological models. In November he was at Murchison's right hand, talking about the opening up of trade with China. In December he sat next to Major Clarke who invited him to visit the United Service Museum. The paper at the Society was given by Lyell on American geology, especially in the region of the Niagara Falls from which he had recently returned. Sopwith also encountered Ruskin and on the following Sunday enjoyed the paintings of J.M.W. Turner and other water colours on Ruskin's walls. In April 1843 there was a further paper by Lyell and in May the diary refers the reader to the transactions of the Geological Society. It is almost as if a chapter is over. He dines at the Club on November 5th 1845 but professional activities have taken him elsewhere. Geological interests were of course not forgotten but his own input had been more recently directed towards models, mapping and the museum of Practical (or Economic) Geology, of which more later.

One final point to record about the Geological Society of London is the meeting on December 2nd 1842. It was a special general meeting which soured the recollections which the diaries normally recorded. As had begun to emerge on November 29th, the council of the Society was under fire from Mr. Charlesworth who hoped to become Secretary and Curator of the Society, replacing Lonsdale. Proceedings continued for some five hours; the Council's decisions were endorsed and Sopwith for one deeply disliked Charlesworth's "want of taste and judgement in his cross-examination of the president"[18] Later, in a long summary of the event of 1842, he again refers to "the violent and injudicious conduct of Mr. Charlesworth [who] savagely slandered the brightest ornaments of the society". Mr. Forbes was unanimously elected instead. In Sopwith's eyes, the council had been vindicated.

* * *

Science was well served by its geologists in the first half of the 19th century. This was not a universal view as Puseyism or New-man-ia would demonstrate, not least against the person of William Buckland.* More striking still was the contribution to Science by the British Association for Advancement of Science. There were plenty of traditional churchmen or academics who might feel threatened or at least question the advance of science as a panacea or focus of intellectual strength. Such might have slumbered or remained embattled behind their traditional tracts of wisdom, poured forth by one parson John Bull to another or to his secular flock. The platform presented by the British Association was a more challenging and dangerous springboard for the claims of science as the philosophy of the age. Even more potentially damaging was the argument of utility in an age facing up to Benthamite utilitarianism and the new "godless institution of Gower Street" founded in 1828. Those who sought to bridge the gap between theology and nature represented no less a threat to the school of christian thinking which followed the teachings of New-man. No, the evidence of natural theology and the argument from design was inferior, contributing nothing to the great eschatological questions of death, judgement, heaven and hell, which poet and priest sought to express anew in a revival of Catholicism.

Paradoxically the cause of science as an academic pursuit may have been weakened by the British Association which sought to publicise and popularise the advances. The argument of utility did not commend itself to the philosophers of the age, churchmen or not, and academics were as aware then as now that practical engineers should be kept in their place. On the whole academics failed to do this and the Great Exhibition of 1851 celebrated the advances of practical science. Yet it was not alone the concept of

---

* The *great chain of History* – William Buckland and the *English School of Geology (1814-49)* by N. A. Rupke OUP Clarendon 1983. This draws attention to what was regarded as Buckland's hearty vulgarity as well as his dangerous latitudinarianism.

the academic against the practical which might restrict the success of the BAAS. There was something of gentlemen versus players: "engineers were restricted to judiciously managed appearances in order to reinforce the claims of science" state Morrell and Thackray in their account of the BAAS under the beguiling title *Gentlemen of Science.** There seems little doubt that Sopwith was a player but increasingly through the 1830s made a strong bid to run with the gentlemen and ultimately be recognised as an honorary gentleman, a Scientist by adoption. Science, as represented by learned societies, did not begrudge his membership; F.G.S. (1835) F.R.S. (1845) M.A. (1857) alongside M.I.C.E,. his certificate of professional status of which he was very proud, and Telford medallist too. It may be observed that of the three other distinguished surveyor-geologists – William Smith, John Farey and Robert Bakewell – none became Fellows of the Geological Society. Later in his career he had the honour to sponsor W.G. Armstrong for membership of the Royal Society. Armstrong, he recalled, liked to put the letters M.D. after his name when in Allendale. They stood for "Maister of the Drallikers", a title bestowed on him by an Allendale miner who saw him putting in the hydraulic engines in the dale. That was the sort of deference Sopwith appreciated, in praise of the master craftsman.

Two major features of Sopwith's claim to be a scientist remain to be studied: his part in the British Association and his election to the Royal Society. The BAAS had been in action since 1831 and the earliest efforts by Babbage to emphasise applied science and mechanical arts made little progress. After Buckland's presidency

---

* *Gentlemen of Science* – the *Early Years of the British Association for the Advancement of Science* by T. Morrell and A. Thackray OUP Clarendon 1981.The chapters on the Ideologies of Science and the Politics of Science are particularly illuminating. John Thackray, librarian and archivist to the Geological Society suggests that in that society was an inner elite, an outer group and a number of local experts. This can probably be mirrored in the BAAS too.

of the Association at Oxford in 1832 the next meeting did not occur at Manchester, a manufacturing centre, as Babbage hoped. Such a location had to wait but the 1835 Dublin meeting brought together a number of engineers who had already contributed papers. A sub-section of Section A (mathematics and physics) for mechanical science applied to the arts emerged that year and in 1836 at Bristol the new Section G for mechanical sciences was created. As Whewell re-defined the relation between science and practice, whereby empirical art begat superior theoretical science and science begat scientific art (a formula acceptable to theorist, manufacturer and self-made engineer), the politics of science began to become clearer.[19] Papers on Cornish steam engines were appropriate for a Bristol meeting. Civil Engineers too responded to the opportunity as suggested in their royal charter of 1828 to "directing the great sources of power in nature for the use and convenience of man" and bridging the concerns of the natural philosopher and the working mechanic.[20] Even if the new Section G was dominated by academics with practising engineers providing the secretariat or local engineers being permitted vice-presidential status, there were gains for all parties. Resources and research were supplied by engineers such as Fairbairn. Railway companies co-operated to allow geological study, a subject of great importance to Sopwith, and many other experiments on materials. Engineers and manufacturers could also provide spectacular events and evening lectures concurrent with the meetings. They might also be involved in lobbying the government, but as has been pointed out elsewhere "of the nineteen successful lobbies in the years 1831–44, only two reflected the concerns of Section G and were promoted partly by engineers: the fate of railway section records urged by Vignoles and of mining records by Buddle and Sopwith".[21] Against this background must be set the events of the Newcastle meeting of the Association in 1838 as recorded by Sopwith.

The first signs of activity were committee meetings for the impending arrival of the British Association: these were on May

19th and May 23rd. At the same time he was writing his guide to
Newcastle (May 25th). On May 26th he learned that £300 would
be needed in subscriptions to meet the expense of fitting up lecture
and dinner rooms and to provide accommodation for "illustrious
strangers, 'Kings of Science' etc.".[22] Professor Phillips came to
inspect the rooms on August 3rd, the same day as Sopwith finished
his little guidebook for the town. The Reception Committee, meeting on August 16th, decided that each member should wear "a red
riband at the breast of his coat".[23] The general local committee
decided that seven shillings and sixpence was a suitable price for
dinner tickets. John Taylor and Lord Cole, familiar to him from
Geological Society meetings, were helping with the plans and the
latter visited Sopwith's offices to look at fossils, plans, models and
sections. The guidebook was published the next day, preparations
continued and the Eighth meeting of the British Association opened
on August 20th.

The diary gives a limited picture of the Association's meetings
but Sopwith used every occasion he could to further his interests
and acquaintances. 1838 was the year in which a second edition of
his treatise on Isometric Drawing was produced: at the suggestion
of Mr. Babbage he wrote a paper before breakfast on August 20th
describing the isograph. He read this and also his description of the
arrangement of writing tables in the Mechanical Section of the
meeting. He went to hear Garnett's paper on the Telegraph before
writing up a report for the *Times*. Mrs Buckland was taken to see
the philosophical library and he went to the Mayoress' ball in the
evening. Buddle's paper on Coalfields with a geological map by
Sopwith of the Coal and Lead Mining districts was read the next
day in the Geological section: the Bucklands, Count Breunner of
Vienna, Dr William Smith of Scarborough and Mr. Dickinson
dined with Thomas and Jane before attending the meeting in the
Central Exchange. Two papers were written out before breakfast
on August 22, further visits were paid to the Geological section and
model room where he had several exhibits and in the evening a

family group including the Hindhaughs, his sister and brother-in-law, went to the Promenade in the Green Market.

The breakfast party on Thursday was a key gathering for Sopwith, hosting over twenty guests including the Bucklands, Count Breunner and Count Hoyas, also of the Austrian mines service, who stayed with the Sopwiths for the week. So did Dr Smith, Mr. Thomas Dickinson of Alston and Miss Dod of Belford, perhaps to keep Jane company. Also listed at breakfast were Ehrenberg of Berlin, Babbage, Charles Barry the architect of the Houses of Parliament, Dr Reid of Edinburgh, Sir Charles Lemon of Carclew and John Taylor, W.C. Trevelyan and other local friends from Alston or Newcastle made up the rest of the party. A similar party gathered on Friday 24th: there were visits to Hancock's natural history collection, a chance to write up some notes on Breunner's description of the Imperial Schools of Mines in Austria and a trip in a gig out to Falfield and Pensher quarry for Barry and Sopwith. Barry was still searching for suitable stone for the rebuilding of the Palace of Westminster. They observed a railway collision near the Victoria bridge at the opening ceremony and shortly after met George Stephenson, William Brandling, James Walker (president of the Institution of Civil Engineers) and Nicholas Wood.

It was in the evening that no time was lost on the question of how to bring "the subject of an Application to Government on Mining Records fairly before the British Association".[24] Buckland, Lemon and Sopwith were closeted from soon after 9 p.m. until 1 a.m. drawing up resolutions and a list of the committee. The Council adopted both these the next day. The Committee consisted of 17 names, headed by the Marquis of Northampton, including the names of Lyell and the professors of Geology at Oxford, Cambridge, London and Durham and was completed by the addition of de la Beche, John Taylor, John Buddle and Thomas Sopwith. It was as well the little lobby group had worked hard: there was such pressure of business in the Geological Section that Sopwith never got a chance to read either of his papers, namely on the Mining

District of Alston Moor and on the Preservation of Mining Records. However his exhibits were on show, the Forest of Dean model taking pride of place, and the "Kings of Geology" paid due attention to it. Sir Charles Lemon presided over the General Committee "with great ability": Lord Cole and Sir Philip Egerton then walked up to Sopwith's house to see the monocleid desk. Lemon breakfasted with him on Sunday: St. Nicholas' Church was so crowded that they went to the organ gallery. The Bishop of Durham preached. In the evening Mr. Ions obligingly came to play the piano.

After a busy pre-breakfast session on Monday August 27th (Sedgwick, Richard Griffith of Dublin, the Bucklands and J.S. Menteith, knowledgeable on Dumfries geology, were at breakfast), eight members of the new mining records committee met at his office. A memorial was drawn up and Sir Charles Lemon transmitted it to Spring Rice, the Chancellor of the Exchequer. Sopwith still had things to show to Buckland in the form of the furniture warerooms before they went to the Natural History dinner. This was held in the Riding School where the Association had dined in the previous week. On the way they saw a balloon being filled up in Green Court. Distinguished friends remained in the offing over the next few days: Greenough, Professor Peacock of Cambridge and Murchison were all paying calls or attending other meetings. Plans for a Newcastle botanical garden and Brunel's lecture on the Thames Tunnel were on the agenda at the Philosophical Society on August 28th.

The meetings over, the British Association dispersed. It had been a useful and proud occasion for a son of Newcastle and Babbage's dream of an exhibition of models of mechanical contrivances, philosophical instruments and products of manufacturing industry had taken place, with full contributions from Sopwith. There was no real break in scientific acquaintance but the Association's meetings had focused all his interests before he plunged back into his professional work. He was now Commissioner for Dean Forest

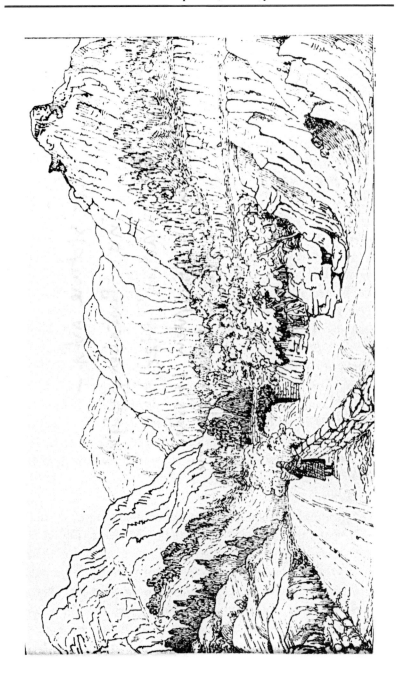

Pont Aberglaslyn 1841.

and a busy time both there and in Ireland, on the mines of County
Clare, lay ahead during the rest of the year. The Association's
meeting at York in 1844 saw a renewal of many friendships marked
by an occasion of absurdity: the Dean of York read a superficial
paper to the geological section to which Sedgwick gave a crushing
reply. Superficial or not, geologists were worried that the progress
of the past few years could be dismissed so easily by a leading
churchman. It was possible to slip back to Newcastle in the midst
of events. Dinners given by Earl Fitzwilliam and by the Archbishop
of York were much enjoyed, as was a fine lecture by the Earl of
Rosse on the subject of his telescope. It was probably a more
relaxed meeting for Sopwith who had no significant axes to grind
this time.

The final accolade to be received by Thomas Sopwith in the field
of science was that of fellowship of the Royal Society. This itself
probably brought about other invitations and recognition, region-
ally and nationally, amounting to membership of twenty-six societies* in the list he records in 1856. The moment of entry to the
Royal Society is clearly recorded: the precise circumstances are
less clear. His reputation had continued to rise under the tutelage
of Buckland, de la Beche and Northampton as he pressed his claims
as geologist and engineer at the highest levels. His prowess as
geological model-maker brought him literally into the presence of
kings and princes.† At this point it is only necessary to mark the
steps towards the "blue ribbon" of science.[25]

Glaciology continued to grip the leading geologists of the day
after Agassiz' theories became widely known. Buckland, an early
opponent, had been converted by 1840 and Lyell also wrote in
favour. Conybeare, Greenough, Murchison and especially de la
Beche remained opposed, the last named deploring Lyell's method-
ology and theoretical pretensions.‡ Sopwith, who accompanied

---

*   See appendix v.

†   See chapter 14 below.

‡   See P. J. McCartney, *Henry de la Beche*, RHL Ltd. Cardiff 1977

Buckland on searches for glacial evidence, supported him at this stage, but whether he followed Buckland's adaptation in the iceberg theory is less clear and in any event immaterial. He was by now receiving due admiration for his geological models by Lyell and Murchison, by Greenough and de la Beche. The models were on show frequently at his house to all comers as well as being set before the Institution of Civil Engineers at which the Telford medal (silver) was awarded to their creator. A fatherly eye was cast upon the beginnings of the Museum of Economic Geology and he frequently visited it in 1840–1. In 1843 he produced his "Account of the Museum of Economic Geology and Mining Records Office". This gave due credit to de la Beche's submission to the Chancellor of the Exchequer about the ordnance survey, Lord Duncannon's go-ahead and the appointment of Richard Phillips F.R.S. as curator.

The Dean Forest model and a set of twelve geological models were shown to the Prince Consort by Buckland on May 5th 1842. The prince was pleased to see them and to receive Sopwith's report on the Duchy of Cornwall mines near Radstock. Lord Northampton was holding a number of soirées at the Royal Society about this time: Sopwith was invited to one on May 7th where the Dean Forest model was again on show. At a second soirée attended by him where he had hoped to meet Prince Albert he was able to talk about his Ebbw Vale and Sirhowy model. His Royal Highness did not attend after all. However introduction was made at a soirée in 1844 on March 8th. The geological models, the surveys of the Duchy of Cornwall mines and recent work in Belgium, not forgetting to mention King Leopold's interests in developments were all discussed with the prince.

Admission to the Royal Society finally occurred on June 19th 1845. The certification for Election shows that the proposal was made on April 3rd 1845 from general knowledge by Edward Sabine. The list of names of proposers from personal knowledge was headed by Buckland and the majority were geologists. The candidate is described in the appropriate spaces as author of the

Treatise on Isometric Drawing and Inventor and Improver of Methods of representing Mineral Structure by dissected models. On the day of admission the president, the Marquis of Northampton, was absent and Professor Owen, a proposer, was in the chair. In the re-written diary entry some years later Sopwith states, "If this, under any circumstances be deemed an honour I think it is still more so when brought about – as my admission has been by direct invitation of, and persuasion of The President and by the unasked for suffrages of so many eminent Fellows".[26] Eleven years after the event he wrote, "There is perhaps no circumstance in my life to which I can look back with greater satisfaction", at the same time rejoicing at his membership of the Athenaeum, which had taken place in 1852, and of the Royal Society of Arts.

If 1845 marks a major turning point in Sopwith's career, it is not because of the Fellowship of the Royal Society. As already indicated, other albeit lesser honours and distinctions were to come. Before considering 1845, the important year of change and the reasons for it, it is appropriate to continue the tale of the surveyor using the diary record. The diary is curiously reinforced by a shorter manuscript which came to light more recently, a working notebook of 1840. It is this which forms the basis of a rather different chapter, one which makes no attempt to be thematic.

Chapter 13

1840 – the Professional's Notebook

The year 1840 is mid-way through one of the most successful decades of Thomas Sopwith's life and possibly one of the busiest or most varied periods. The distinction of his appointment as Commissioner under the Dean Forest Award gave him further respect; the British Association visit to Newcastle of 1838 had led to work on mining records and the founding of the Geological Society's Museum and these projects were now under way; travel to London, Dean Forest, Wales and more locally, over to Alston, took place; old friendships were renewed and new ones made. The reason for choosing the year 1840 for separate study is a more prosaic one. When the diary was written it is probable that other notebooks were used as a source of information and presumably as a day by day record. Some of the diary or journal, which runs to 168 surviving small volumes, was written up a few days after the event. The writer often records at the head of the page where he wrote it, giving a date. Sometimes he adds a note a few years later and as early as 1842 there are parts which were either extended or summarised as late as 1876. However only one example of what could have been a series of preliminary notebooks has come to light: this is a notebook for 1840.*

---

* The survival of the notebook is of interest. Its existence was made known to me by letter following an article written in the Wellington College Year Book for 1973. A cousin, Mr. K. O. Shelford, member of an equally successful engineering family doubly intermarried with Sopwith's through Thomas' son

The notebook is about four inches high and seven and a half inches wide. The pages are marked up in a standard form throughout, repeating the marking in the following order. Page one is the most informative, divided into 7 parts horizontally one for each day of the week. Vertical divisions show the zodiacal day symbol for the day of the week, and give the month and date. A narrow column follows showing symbols for the state of the weather in a three stage day, with sufficient room to show marked contrasts within those stages. The next column shows the number of miles travelled on days where travel occurs and a running total for the year appears against the Sunday entry. A space of five and a half inches by about half an inch remains to record the main events of each day, a space in which the day is sometimes broken into three parts.

On the reverse of the page are two columns for cash received and cash paid out, a balance being struck and carried forward. The first entries show a payment from Mr. Hindhaugh, his brother-in-law, perhaps rent or for professional services rendered, a sum of £40. Cash was paid out to Mr. Stokes, dentist of whom he writes most approvingly for work done (for £1.5s.0d.) on January 3rd, Sopwith's 37th birthday. A later visit on January 16th for an extraction which broke the tooth ended a pain he had endured for several weeks. The other two payments in the first week of January were to Marcus Scott his assistant surveyor (£5 on account) and to his wife Jane for housekeeping (£15). The next payments for this latter purpose were on January 27th (£40) and February 22nd (£30). The payment to Jane on May 15th of £75 on account seems to be for other purposes but housekeeping is met by a sum of £30 to £50 per month.

Arthur and daughter Anna, had it in his possession in Grenada, W.I. At the time of the first *coup d'état* in the late 1970s, the notebook was safely returned to England. English visitors to the island who had been marooned near the airport in a state of near-siege sought to repay Mr. Shelford for his kindness in providing asylum for them. He responded by asking them to bring the notebook home to England.

Opposite the cash balances, which are totalled and carried forward to the next series, there are pages which are used for a variety of matters. Headed 'From' and 'To' they appear to be for recording incoming and outgoing letters and in some weeks this occurs. Frequently they are left blank, occasionally a journey is summarised or some other note made such as a decision to start a job or recall an assistant. Incoming letters are by no means all recorded and the pages are largely unused, although neatly numbered from 1 to 20 (under 'From') and 21 to 40 (under 'To'). A more exciting entry appears enlarging on the events of February 6th when sparks were seen coming from the new workshop. In fact the sparks came from the chimney while Ralph Renwick, Thomas Robson and two or three others were finishing the making of a coffin at the late hour of 11 p.m. The first of the 'From' and 'To' pages have some more accounts on them, including some rents. There also appears a list of colours at between one shilling and two shillings in price which might be paints for use in sketching or for plans and levels. Indigo, cobalt and sepia head a list of eight colours, pencilled in. A list of rents paid to Mr. Grainger between November 1835 and November 1839 totals £101.

On the reverse of this page appears three columns. The first has the zodiacal sign for the day and space to put appointments for which it is occasionally used. The centre column is headed by the date, written in, of the first day of the week recorded on the previous pages. Below this is printed, in copper-plate italic style, "Thomas Sopwith, Newcastle on Tyne", followed by the number of the week and thirteen numbered lines. These are sometimes used for recording business papers or other current subjects. The third column continues the numbering from the previous page, from 42 to 60, and is again frequently empty of information. The first of the pages in this series is exceptional in recording revenues totalling £1881.11.0, over £1400 of which refer to Sir Edward Blackett and the Commissioners of Woods and Forests.

The final version of the journal covers 1840 in volumes 23 to

25 and the first twenty-five pages of volume 26. The 1840 notebook gives the bare outline of events but it is probable that the information given was sufficient for the journal entries which are themselves often sketchy and even dull in their brevity. Descriptions of the landscape blossom whereas topics of conversation are seldom identified or examined. The pleasure for the reader comes largely from acquaintance with people, places, music and scenery and most positive that pleasure is because the writer is for the most part well content with his experience. The jottings in the notebook are of course brief and factual but not without interest in their own right. On June 20th the notebook records "Across River on Iron Bar". He was staying in Bristol and crossed the Avon gorge from pier to pier of the proposed suspension bridge. The full diary states, "I crossed the River Avon on the iron bar from pier to pier and narrowly escaped an accident – the prospect was truly sublime".[1] On this occasion he also drew a sketch in his journal showing a tiny car hanging below the iron bar or wire along which he was presumably hauled. What would Jane have thought of it? She was miles away in Newcastle, looking after five children, the most recent arrival being Anna in April 1840, and managing the housekeeping.

Following the year through, the winter months show activity in the vicinity of Newcastle. The weather was fine at first but wet at the end of the month of January. Sopwith was busy in the office most days with social evenings at the homes of Donkin, Armstrong and Hancock.* There was a theatre visit on January 6th and the Mayor's ball on the 7th. There were also meetings of the Joiners' Company and of a committee to form a Botanical and Zoological garden. The latter gathering asked him to sketch the proposed gardens which he did a few days later. The main business at the office was a mining report for Colonel Heth for a proposed

---

* Armorer Donkin and William Armstrong were partners in the law firm of Donkin, Stable and Armstrong. Sopwith frequently enjoyed their friendship and hospitality as also that of John and Mary Hancock in whose natural history collection he took a close interest.

development in Virginia, U.S.A. Messrs. Hall and Forster had just returned with details which were considered carefully by Sopwith together with John Buddle and Robert Stephenson. The latter read over Sopwith's draft report of 21st January approvingly and the journal comments on the valued friendship which he enjoyed with Stephenson.

February 1st was the ninth anniversary of Thomas and Jane's wedding day. Hindhaughs and Burnups came to dinner and Benjamin and Marcus Scott also came during the evening. Wet weather and a cold prevented a visit to Otterburn on February 4th but he was soon meeting friends again, Robert Hawthorn, engineer, and Joseph Crawhall on successive evenings. February 10th was another special day. Accorded capital letters in the notebook is the wedding of Queen Victoria and Prince Albert. It was a holiday and Sopwith spent it "in painting landscapes in opake (sic) colours at Mrs Hancock's". Newcastle put on a "very splendid exhibition of fireworks at the Parade ground from 8 till 10 o'clock".[2] February 14th was a bright and sunny day, much more suited for his visit to Otterburn in the Chevy Chase coach with William Burnup. They rode a further six miles to Woodburn where he made sketches of two or three Roman altars recently discovered on Mr. Shanks' land, along with one silver and twelve copper coins. In his diary Sopwith waxed eloquent on the day, remembering Walter Scott's description of Woodburn as well as enjoying a good meal at Otterburn and looking approvingly at nearly twelve miles of the road he had designed, but not seen, ten years before.

During the rest of the month there was work in the office, the showrooms and at Wallsend, especially seeing John Buddle, possibly over plans for the next visit to Dean Forest. On Monday February 17th letter-writing was put in hand, after rising at 5 a.m., until 9 o'clock. This work was done in the library, sitting at his monocleid desk. Domestic bliss for Jane ended abruptly as Thomas set off on Sunday February 23rd at 4 o'clock in the train to Carlisle. Writing over a month later, he comments on Jane's particular grieving. Appreciating her affection and admitting that he enjoyed the business and occupations when at home he also knew how adaptable he was when away. Travel was always exciting: the scenery, the novelty of his professional duties and the friendship and hospitality which he met everywhere made for a happy life.[3] On Monday a nine hour journey on the Glasgow Mail took Buddle and Sopwith to Preston: here Buddle went on to Merthyr Tydfil via Birmingham while Sopwith went to T.M. Mackay's in Upper Parliament Street, Liverpool. He investigated Mr Adcock's new mine pump described as a 20 inch fan, able to raise 60 gallons per minute some 40 feet high up a zinc pipe. Costs and dimensions impressed him and he was glad to have seen the experiment. Business took him to Chester and Holywell on Wednesday concerning a mine at Llansannon but he had time to look around both at Holywell and Chester where he found the Cathedral somewhat decayed. He played some psalms on the organ and commented both on Harrison's great stone-arched bridge and the shop arcades, one of which he sketched in the journal. On Friday he was at Cheltenham with the Probyns and off to see a landslip near Aggs Hill. At Bristol on Saturday there was more business with his generous friend Mr. Isaac Cooke, concerning the Blaendau colliery. Several pages are devoted to describing the disciplined life of Mr. Cooke, a solicitor whose day starts at 3 or 4 a.m. with a ten mile walk before prayers and breakfast. He walks two miles to his office, working for eight hours before walking back for dinner. He than rides in a fly to the office for two more hours work and walks back to tea at 10 o'clock. Sopwith accompanied Mr. Cooke on his pre-breakfast exercise on Monday March 2nd and admitted in his journal that compared with this 69 year old paragon he felt himself to be "an insignificant cypher and blush for days and weeks and months lost in comparative indolence and inactivity".[4]

The fine weather which had made his journey so pleasant continued through the first two weeks of March. He was hardly at Coleford on March 2nd before he was dashing up to London to secure the re-appointment of Mr. Thomas Graham, clerk to the Mining Commissioners of Dean Forest, whose resignation is described as being very inconvenient. The visit to London needed careful negotiation with reports to Milne and to Lord Duncannon at the Office of Woods and Forests but it was ultimately successful. Along the banks of the river he describes the Wye coracles or truckles used by salmon fishermen: in London itself there are friends to see and business to be done. Mr. Milne's monocleid arrived on March 6th so its proud inventor helps set up the desk in Milne's office.

Back at Coleford the Dean Forest Commissioners' work filled the days until March 18th, perhaps explaining why the journal was not written up until March 25th when he could do justice to an account of a lecture by Dr Buckland whom he had heard on March 7th, in a break in this journey back to Dean Forest. "The intricate and perplexing business of the Forest",[5] together with railway discussions with Edward Protheroe and Captain Moorsom of the Birmingham and Gloucester Railway, was followed by business at Pontypool. Unfortunately Sopwith experienced a tightness of the chest and the recommendation of a Mr. Essex to apply 12 leeches encouraged him to make his way to the comfort of Bristol rather than risk entering Blaendau mines. The pain had subsided a little by the time he had reached Newport on March 23rd where he characteristically nosed round the Westgate Hotel. Here on November 4th in the previous year Chartist rioters had tried to break in. Soldiers obligingly showed him various bullet holes and described how the mayor had opened the shutters and tried to address the mob. After reliving the excitement and by taking a good walk Sopwith felt much better but caught the Glamorgan steamboat to Bristol nevertheless. He put up at the Gloster Hotel, Clifton and Mr. Cooke soon called and obligingly summoned a surgeon by the name of Seagur.

The stay at Clifton under Seagur's care was a welcome break from his labours. Music and sketching were his occupations. Isaac

Cooke's sons lived nearby and Isaac Cooke junior's house had been the home of the celebrated Hannah More in her last years. Sopwith sketched the view from the window of a room adjoining the front drawing-room. By April Sopwith was much better and able to return to London. His surgeon's fees are recorded in the notebook, one guinea to Mr. Essex and five pounds to Mr. Seagur. Mrs Ord told him that his ill-health was "wholly owing to my long walks in the mornings".[6] He was thrilled to join a party of Milne's to visit the Italian Opera and was allowed to look backstage and so appreciate the design before settling into Box 24 to hear Persiani sing *La Sonnambula*, a work he had heard Malibran perform twice before. Queen Victoria and Lady Normanby arrived after Act 1, adding to the occasion, and the diarist writes at length both about the theatre and the Queen's enjoyment of the evening but prefers to quote the *Morning Chronicle* on the subject of the music itself. He admits to such a passion for music that he reflects it is just as well he can only play by ear or else he would be chained to the organ.

By April 11th the business at Blaendau was resumed. He was underground viewing the Rock and Meadow vein and examining documents until midnight, writing up two reports. Back on Dean Forest business until April 24th he left Newnham at 2 o'clock reaching Birmingham by 12.30 a.m. Leaving Birmingham at 2 a.m. by the London train he reached Preston at 7 a.m. and by mail coach reached Carlisle at 4.30 p.m. The final stretch of the 320 mile journey ended at 8 p.m. It had cost £8 including refreshment and tips. He arrived some thirty-two hours after the birth of Anna to find that Jane and the new baby were well. He bought himself a new hat at Wilson's for one guinea.

The fine weather had brought on the vegetation in the north of England as far as that seen in Gloucestershire. The weather broke on May 7 and was poor for ten days when Sopwith was working either at home or in the office on various reports, particularly dealing with mines on the Haltwhistle estate. He was shown some

July	Miles		
5	31½	At Swansea Church.. Iron Hill.	
6	36	Went at 7h Inn at Prospect.	
7			
8	73	At Swansea all day	
9	35	Survey of Work and Southward	
10	24	Do	do
11	20	Do	do
	3,3,3,5		

screw moorings in the form of a large iron plate 3 foot in diameter which by a shaft and capstan could be sunk up to 16 feet into the river bed. There was a visit to Holy Island to look at ways of improving the harbour on May 28th and 29th. June 1st was pronounced to be very warm. It was an important day for the journal records and has sketches of the proposed geological models which he had been thinking about and which will be referred to in a later chapter (see ch 14).

Jane was loth to see him go off to London and the Forest of Dean. He attended a meeting of the Geological and Polytechnic Society at the Cutlers' Hall at Sheffield en route, giving a lecture and demonstration of geological models. He stayed at Spital Hill belonging to Mr. T. Sorby and made a sketch of the house. In London there was some Newcastle Corporation business as well as renewing acquaintance with Charles Babbage and his calculating machine and with J.C. Loudon whose daughter showed him a number of her woodcuts. On one day, June 8th "a very splendid procession of teetotallers" passed by "their banners were truly magnificent – they were said to be ten thousand in number".[7] Payments in the notebook show that a sum of £515 was received from the Office of Woods and paid over to W.S. Potter Esq, witnessed by Mr. Donkin, solicitor. Notes also indicate an intention to visit Lincoln and Bennett, Hatters, of Sackville Street, Piccadilly.

There was work to be done in the Mendips before Sopwith arrived in Dean Forest once more. At Radford colliery he was obtaining information for the Dean and Chapter of Christ Church Oxford to whom the colliery belonged. On Dean Forest business from June 23rd to July 3rd, he then travelled by Bristol steampacket to Swansea at a cost of £3.5.6d. and did some drawings for a model[*] which he posted off to Newcastle on July 7th. There was a journey to St. Davids principally to survey Mr. B.M. Bright's property near

---

[*] This was probably a model for the Ebbw Vale and Sirhoy ironworks. (see chapter 14)

Nolton Haven and at Southwood, and a long haul back to Newcastle, 450 miles in 48 hours, 37 of them actually on the road or
by rail in eleven different conveyances.

After a few days' business in mid-July, the Sopwiths had some
holiday, visiting friends and relatives at Rothbury, Amble and
Warkworth, staying some of the time at Bustin Barns. There were
pleasant trips up the river from Warkworth to the Hermitage,
sketching and walking. Thomas and Jane were accompanied by
Thomas' sister Mary Hindhaugh in the phaeton belonging to her
husband along with Mary's youngest boy Nat and the Sopwith's
youngest child Anna. Two female servants and one manservant
attended them. Little Mary Jane, the six year old daughter whose
health was never strong, had been at Tynemouth in July but was
presumably left there to continue convalescence. Earlier excursions
in late July mention Ursula's company but Isabella and Thomas,
four and two years old respectively are not mentioned at the time.
Payments in the notebook include sums for music and subscriptions,
for a Bible for Margaret and a long list of expenses on the visit to
Warkworth. These include several tolls: "Dinner, servants and
horses, Morpeth £1; Fruit at Swarland Gardens two shillings; Paid
boys for seeking and finding screw one shilling and sixpence; entry
to the Dairy, School and Castle, totalling six shillings": the list is
completed by payments to servants at Bustin Barns and at Cresswell
and Bothal, together with toll-gate costs on the return journey. By
August 9th the aggregated mileage for the year reached 4000.

On August 21st the Reverend John Allen called at Sopwith's
office, introduced by the Reverend William Turner. Allen was
collecting information for the Educational Committee of the Privy
Council, looking for statistics of morals, education etc. in the
mining district around Newcastle. This was a subject of considerable interest to Sopwith although no details are given at this point.
In 1853 he was to publish a forty-page tract on "Education its
present state" and the "Observations addressed to the miners and
other workmen employed in Mr. Beaumont's Lead Mines in East

and West Allendale and Weardale" (1846) set out plainly his views on the education and progress of those who came under his supervision. The school at Allenheads in which he took so much care has been a field centre pursuing some of the subjects in the locality in which he too was knowledgeable.

Mid-August was a time for letter-writing, local interests and general business. Jane was unwell on August 23rd and they were at home together all day. Thomas was off again on his travels, this time to North Wales in the Denbigh region. He was particularly fond of the scenery in Clwyd and enjoyed a pleasant stay with Sir Henry and Lady Browne at Bronwylfa. Browne had in his collection "a travelling road book and map of France used by Napoleon" as well as a "French Field Marshall's baton covered with bees, of silver gilt".[8] Colonel Browne had shrewdly forwarded his chances of promotion by taking a tutor to teach him Spanish while he was in Portugal which brought him into close contact with the Duke of Wellington in the successful Spanish campaigns. After seven years as a lieutenant he rose in three years to be a lieutenant colonel. The main purpose of Sopwith's visit was to value the collieries at Argoed and Buckley, but he inevitably enjoyed an introduction to the organist at St. Asaph's Cathedral and at Bodryddan met Miss Anghared Lloyd, reputed to be one of the best Welsh scholars. The notebook entry for August 31st mentions glow-worms on the turnpike road but the diary entry written nearly a month later ignores them in favour of writing at some length about Mr. John Taylor at Coed Ddu, a summer residence from where he could supervise Flint Lead Mines, one of many mining interests represented elsewhere in Cornwall, Ireland and Mexico.

In early September, after business near Shifnal, Sopwith was up in London again. Acquaintance was renewed with Loudon, Clegg's atmospheric railway and Robert Davison. The subject of education brought an important new introduction, to Dr. Kay, the secretary to the Committee of the Privy Council on Education. Sopwith had drawn a chart showing the religious institutions of Newcastle which presumably was a basis for information on the morals of the mining districts. He was also introduced to Mr. Matthew Greenlees of Glasgow to whom he showed the principal improvements in Newcastle when they had travelled north on September 11th. Armorer Donkin supplied some useful statistics of the mining population in his letters so Sopwith was able to pass these on to the Revd. John Allen. On September 18th there was another sad visit to Mary Jane at Tynemouth. It is not stated with whom she was staying but sea air was supposed to be improving her chances of survival. It made little impact however: she eventually died in 1842.

The final visit to the Forest of Dean in 1840 began on September 24th. The notebook records a sum of £5.0.6d. paid out without giving other details but in the journal it is noted that 120 miles were by coach and 150 miles by railway. Inside coach travel, including payments to drivers, guards, porters and places of refreshment cost 5 pence per mile while railway travel, excluding refreshment, cost 3 pence per mile. Buddle and Sopwith found their fellow commissioner Probyn unwell on several occasions during the visit. Business was transacted at Newnham and visits made to the iron mines near Wigpool on the northern edge of the forest. After both Buddle and Sopwith had dealt with other business at Newport they moved base to Coleford on October 5th. The two succeeding days were devoted entirely to Dean Forest Commissioners' business indoors from 9 a.m. to 10 p.m. On the way home they had a chance to travel on the American-built engine from Cheltenham, the Victoria No.84, which achieved an average of nearly 30 m.p.h. on a seven-mile stretch. On the journey the travellers met other engineers: Forster, an assistant to Stephenson; John Stevenson, a contractor paying out some £3000 in wages each week, and George Stephenson himself. George was travelling to Chesterfield and was full of information about his mining speculation near that town.

Well-known Newcastle figures feature in the notebook in mid-October. With Miss Mary Hancock he visited Thomas Bewick's daughter and admired a large number of woodblocks of the great artist. Richard Grainger spent much of the morning of October 16th with him talking about the re-arrangement of the Sopwith ware-rooms in Grey Street. On Wednesday October 21st the notebook records a visit to Seghill with W.G. Armstrong and W.D. Anderson to make experiments "on the newly discovered electricity in steam".[9] Sopwith wrote a memorandum on the subject for Robert Were Fox, the Cornish scientist: Armstrong sent a statement to Michael Faraday.*

Dr and Mrs Buckland paid a visit in the same month. They stayed in Newcastle en route from Edinburgh on October 27th and on the following day Sopwith made a sketch of the great geologist laden with luggage which was later engraved and used as an illustration in Buckland's biography. The visit whetted Sopwith's own appetite for specimen-hunting on Hartside for terebratula and encrinites.

The notebook at this point has fewer entries and in the journal the rest of the year through November and December is summa-rised with references to matters of interest in the previous ten months. In the notebook at the end of September he recorded cash received and paid out but no longer did he make totals or carry forward the sum from the bottom of the page. Life was a little fuller in the week starting November 29th with dining out, lectures and theatre visits as well as Anna's christening at All Saints Church on December 3rd followed by a party for twenty people at home. Although the notebook makes no mention of it, Thomas decided to learn music and suffered a rare reverse on which he enlarges in the diary. It was after all much better to play by ear and Mr. Ions the organist at St. Nicholas' church was no longer requested to give lessons. A very different plan which was discussed with John Hancock also did not bear fruit but was doubtless one stage in thinking about a new museum. On December 17th Hancock was at Sopwith's workshops and it was proposed to put up a new building

---

*   See chaper 12 p. 152

in Sandyford Road which would have dwelling rooms on the ground floor and a large room 80 feet by 36 feet above to house Hancock's collection of stuffed birds.

The end of the year is recorded as plainly as any other time. Work in the office or at the workshops goes on without pausing to celebrate Christmas. The notebook for December 25th records, "At workshops. Geological Models made by Liddle. Dined at Mr. Hindhaughs".[10] He was at home on December 26th but back in the office writing reports on the succeeding Monday until the end of the year. Mindful of the sparks seen at the workshops earlier in the year, the payments recorded to the Newcastle Fire office on two separate policies were doubtless wise precautions. There is also a payment to the Norwich Union Office for Life Insurance. The final note of the book, written in pencil, looks like a reminder. Perhaps Jane, whose name and interests seldom appear in notebook or diary, has the last word. The note says, "Portuguese plums. See (?) Hoovery. Send some if he can get them but no French Plums".

Chapter 14

Maps, Models and Mining Records

Maps and plans are the common currency of the surveyor dealing as he does with pictorial representations of route-ways, shapes of fields and other details of man's development of the land. It is not surprising to discover that the limitations of existing plans available to Sopwith caused him to think about improving them. The skills which he possessed for recording accurately the subjects of his work led to his most important achievement, and since his surveying took him increasingly underground, the expertise was needed in the service of the mining surveyor and engineer. So it was that the thinking and practice devoted to mining operations developed into a marvellous representation not only in three dimensions but also to reveal the secrets of geological strata.

The first map recorded in the journal was a copy which young Thomas made in 1816 of a map of the Roman Wall. It was constructed for a "Mr. Dalton, an itinerant but highly respectable and able lecturer".[1] Plans were doubtless used for work which was done for Newcastle corporation: references to his designs for the town gaol and his study of All Saints' Church Newcastle have already been made. His architectural interests were later revealed in J.C. Loudon's *Architectural Magazine*. The change of career which took him to Alston as a young minerals surveyor also developed two aspects of expertise: in the drawing of mining plans and the use of isometrical projection.

Mining plans had an obvious usefulness to managers of mining

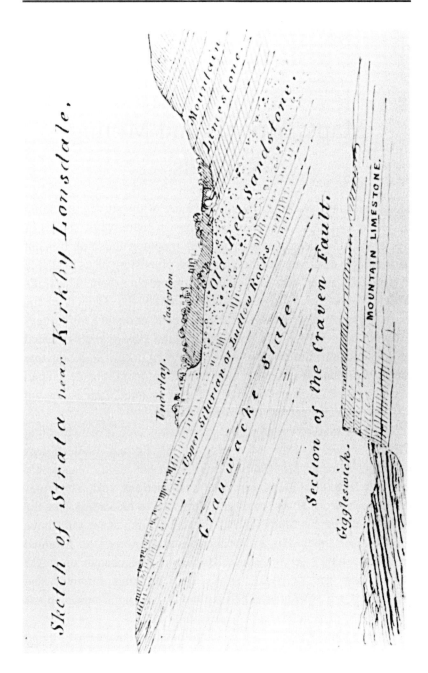

Strata near Kirkby Lonsdale.

concerns: Sopwith believed that they should have a wider currency. In 1828 engraved plans were published by Dickinson and Sopwith, surveyors.[2] There were three plans and sections entitled "Geological Sections of Holyfield, Hudgill Cross Vein and Silver Band Lead Mines in Alston Moor and Teesdale". They were issued from the Loaning House on the edge of Alston town and dedicated to John Taylor FRS, FGS. On September 15th 1828 Dr. Buckland's order for six copies of these plans was received.[3] Sopwith had already sent an example to Walter Calverley Trevelyan for which he was paid six guineas and the correspondence referring to it expresses a hope that he would sell more in Alston Manor itself. In December 1828 a further letter to Trevelyan asks for copies of a paper costing ten shillings and sixpence to be sent to Buckland and others. The charge might cover the costs but he would receive "scarcely any remuneration for the time and labour in surveying, measuring strata etc.".[4]

The published geological sections of Holyfield, Hudgill Cross Vein and Silver Band lead mines are beautifully produced. The levels and veins are picked out in different colours: blue, orange and fawn are used on a plan of Hudgill cross vein while in a similar separate plan of Hudgill Burn, green and pink are used for levels and blue for the veins and strings. In the introduction it is explained that it is important to show "the disposition and changes of strata, the position of veins etc." and with so many non-resident shareholders there was a need to make operations intelligible to them.[5] A detailed description follows of the different rocks – basalt, soft freestone or hazle and limestone – with an explanation of their relationship to the scenery above ground. Notes on the terms used are added. These are very full and clear and the shareholders would certainly be much better informed after perusing them. Veins take their names from the estate through which they pass and neighbouring veins are identified as North, Middle and South or sun; the hade is the leaning from the perpendicular and the throw a disruption of adjoining strata by which they have been raised or depressed on one cheek (side); strings are small veins and flats are cavernous parts of the strata; levels are passages for access, hence horse-levels and water-levels; levels in a different horizontal plane or random are shown in different colours; drifts are similar to levels but cut for discovery or ventilation, terminating in foreheads; rises and sumps are upward and downward workings from a level or drift, often named after the miners who work them. Above ground the bouse or lead ore is deposited in bouse teams from where it is broken by knocking stones, i.e. by hand, or crushed in a water-driven mill. Spoil goes to dead heaps while the ore is further sorted on the washing-floors and again from the sediment in the slime pits. Bings of ore are laid down in the bingstead and eventually go to the smelting-house.

Efficient as the plans and sections were they showed only the first stage of Sopwith's careful observation and recording of mines. The second stage was the use and development of the isometrical projection.[*] Isometrical projection, already used and developed by Professor Farish, was an ideal means of relating sections and plans. Carefully drawn to scale, a three-dimensional view of the ground can be shown without using perspective and therefore maintaining a constant vertical scale. Surveyed detail, which is represented using a square grid on a plan can be transferred to the diamond shapes with the same lengths on the isometric projection.[6] The scale is maintained along the two main directions of the projection, set at an angle of 36° 30' to the plane of the horizon. This has now been adapted to the common angle of 30°. The bird's eye view from above improved an appreciation of a piece of ground but only frequent cross-sections could display the strata-like slices in a marble-cake effect.

The topic of isometric drawing intrigued Sopwith to such an extent that he produced a treatise on it in 1834. A second edition was published in 1838 in which he was careful to give credit to other instrument makers who produced such useful aids as a multameter, a geometric pen and an eidograph. Parallel scales by

[*] See above, chapter 3

Marquoi and Keith were not widely known and nor did he think that Farish's isometric rulers had been manufactured for sale. If Sopwith had not invented parallel rulers he nevertheless felt justified in recommending them as developed by his own hand, and Farish's own commendation merely confirmed their usefulness. Farish had provided the isometric T square or bevel but both in construction and use accuracy was difficult to maintain.[7] There is little doubt that the detailed treatment of the subject did much to advertise its use to the great benefit of all who sought accurate delineation of isometric projection. Once again the craftsman in Sopwith desired to combine art and practicality, whether by using paper and card backed by plane wood or constructing the rulers out of ivory. He was thoroughly conversant with the making and use of the instruments. As far as the journal is concerned, two references to isometric drawing will suffice. The first occurs in September 1834 when it is recorded that the treatise was completed.[8] The second is equally brief: it refers to the proposed railway arrangements which had been discussed with Richard Grainger and an isometric drawing was made to show how these arrangements would fit into the schemes of improvement in Newcastle for which Grainger worked so hard.[9]

The progression from plans and sections to isometrical projection of them was thus an important further stage in Sopwith's work. Yet his ideas did not stop there and his most useful contribution to mining surveys and to the science of geology itself was yet to come. This contribution was the construction of geological models. They were of two types. The first were large models of particular areas of coal and iron-ore workings: the second were smaller models which included coal-seams and the effects of faults upon them but which did not represent actual areas. In both examples, the art of model-making was brought to a new level of competence and the evidence still remains.*

* For a full treatment of the large geological models, see S. Turner and W.R. Dearman in the *Proceedings of the Yorkshire Geolog. Soc.* Vol 44 Part 1 No 1 July 1982.

Models featured in a variety of ways in Sopwith's business and interests, being produced for particular cases before committees of enquiry or courts of law. In 1839 for example a model of the Savings Bank constructed for the trial of Bolam, murderer of Joseph Mellie, was being housed in his Newcastle home one weekend. These ghoulish rooms were a careful replica of the bank with fire damage shown and two little wooden figures along with bloodstains on the wall set amongst the furniture on a scale of two feet to an inch. Several friends came to view this ghastly doll's house before the trial was started on the ensuing Monday. There were probably other models of houses, buildings or streets made for Newcastle corporation or to support ideas of Grainger, but if so, the journal does not refer to them. The materials in the Sopwith workshop were readily available and with his architectural interests, Thomas must have had a hand in the procuring of the business and the design even if cousin John and the regular workforce were given the task of executing the orders. Closer to his own geological interests was a model designed to show the geological structure of the sulphur wells at Harrogate which formed part of the evidence for Mr. Cresswell's recommendation at the trial heard at York on March 14th 1837.

Amongst references to admiration of geological maps such as those of William Smith which Sopwith purchased from Cary's on April 13, 1837 while giving evidence on the London and Brighton railway bill, there begins to emerge an interest in geological models. In 1833 he saw "two very beautiful modelled maps of France and Italy . . . brought from Hamburgh (sic) by Professor Pillans . . . very excellent examples of Topographical modelling, an art which in this country is almost entirely neglected and unknown".[11] It would be interesting to know whether these had any geological data, either in the form of cross-sections or other notes explaining the shapes displayed. As early as 1828 Sopwith had admired three models of Switzerland in the museum housed in the university college of Edinburgh, mentioning "plans and views of mountains, strata etc."

The impetus for constructing a large model to be used in the giving of evidence on the subject of the Forest of Dean is clearly stated. The surveying of the iron and coal mines which had been efficiently done with the use of Sopwith's improved staff had been recorded on sixteen maps or plans and published in 1835. The Dean Forest bill was due to be debated in late 1837 and Sopwith heard about the proposals from Alexander Milne of the Office of Woods. Milne also approved of the suggestion that a model of the Forest "should be prepared to explain the relative position of the veins of coals and workings before the committee in parliament. The cost of such a model might probably be 16 or 20£"[12.] The suggestion had come from Sopwith's fellow-commissioner John Buddle. On October 2nd 1837 directions were being given for the construction of the model and on November 5th the report on the survey had been finished and signed by Buddle and Sopwith. On March 10th 1838 Buddle and Armorer Donkin called to see the Dean Forest model but it is not clear whether it had been finished at this stage. It seems likely that it had been because on March 30th Sopwith was reading a paper on the construction of Geological models and exhibiting the one which he had recently made of Dean Forest. He would not have had time to construct more than one.

The construction of such models was carefully recorded in the second edition of the Treatise on Isometrical Drawing (1838). Sections across the area were drawn to scale on a rectangular grid. The sections were cut out in pasteboard covered with drawing paper or on thin plates of copper. These were painted and could show details in ink and different colours. The sections were then joined criss-cross by half-lapping, i.e. cutting half-way through the thin plates and slotting them in similar cuts on the crossways-set plates. The plates were then placed on a plane surface, the spaces filled with plaster of Paris or wood moulded or curved on top to represent the ground surface. In the Forest of Dean model, lime-wood was used as a light and easy wood to work, infilling the plane-tree grid of sections. The model could be taken apart at the several main coal seams with careful sawing along the line of the seams. With seasoned wood, even a very thin and curved stratum could be represented. Sopwith was pleased with the result and by 1843 there were four large models – two of Dean Forest, one of Ebbw Vale and Sirhowy iron works and one of Nentsberry lead-mining district in Cumberland – of which especial approval was given to the second Forest of Dean model by Sir Henry de la Beche. De la Beche reviewed the model in the collection at the Museum of Practical Geology, of which more later, and this accolade, along with William Buckland's, is an indication from the first director of the geological survey of the value of the new style of model.

The Dean Forest model was on show at the British Association meetings in Newcastle already alluded to in August 1838. Sedgwick and Lyell discussed it in the Geological Section where Sopwith proudly noted that "it occupied a much larger share of attention than any other subject brought forward at the section on this day".[13] Brunel was shown it at about the same time and in the autumn it was on show at Mr. Machin's house, Whitemead Park, where it was explained to a gathering of gentry and ladies before being brought into the practical use for which it was intended, as an aid to the Dean Forest Commissioners in explaining the distribution of resources to interested parties. The model was in London in April 1840 when an explanation of it was given to the Institute of Civil Engineers presided over by Mr. James Walker. In October 1842 it was summoned from Newcastle to Durham to be shown not only to the Bishops of Chester and Durham but also to several professors and their friends, including the Duke of Wellington's brother, Dr Wellesley, and to the engineering students whose papers Sopwith had been examining in the morning. Later in the year a duplicate of the first Dean Forest model was presented to his friend and mentor, Dr William Buckland. Buckland had always shown interest and enthusiasm for Sopwith's mapping skills from the earlier days of the Hudgill Burn plans for the isometric drawing and now for the geological models, great and small. It was thus fitting that Sopwith should return his thanks and admiration in the form of a fine model with a sliding table and top to the one from whose instruction and friendship he had benefited so much.

The Dean Forest model stands as the flagship of Sopwith's large models. The survey of the royal forest was an important national task for the crown and the major means of recognition for Sopwith at the highest professional level. It is perhaps not surprising that there is less reference to the construction of the other large models. One such is a model of Ebbw Vale and Sirhowy Iron Works, possibly made in 1839, but the entry in the journal suggests that he was unfamiliar with the Harfords' business in that region before January of that year. Detailed surveying and a report on it had been completed by March 1839. However there is no significant further mention of Sirhowy and Ebbw Vale until April 1842 when Sopwith attended the soirée of the President of the Geological Society, Roderick Murchison. Here in Murchison's drawing-room is the first mention of a model on show and its creator duly answered questions on it. This model was probably the duplicate of one made for the Harfords and was duly placed in the Museum of Economic Geology in the following year. It was also the subject of a verbal description by Sopwith at the West Riding of Yorkshire Geological and Polytechnic Society meeting in Wakefield in September 1842 where he was glad incidentally to note that there were "no traces of the disturbances which have prevailed in these districts".[14]

Of the other large models created, those of Alt-y-grug, a mountainous mining district in South Wales, Nentsberry, the lead-mining area in Cumberland, and Moel Wyn, made for the Office of Woods and Forests, the evidence is much more sketchy. All three models are listed in the 1875 edition of "Description of Sopwith's Geological Models". Alt-y-grug was surveyed in the company of Mr. Hooper, agent to the Duke of Beaufort. The plans, sections and detail for a model were dispatched to Newcastle on July 7 1840.[15] The finished model is recorded as being for the duke. The area covered by Nentsberry was well-known from the early days of lead-mining apprenticeship in the 1820s at Alston. The area had already been the subject of a large isometrical drawing in the 1838 Treatise on Isometrical Drawing. In July 1843 Sopwith took his assistant Thomas Bewick to point out the ground preparatory to making a model for the Museum of Economic Geology. The journal mentions another request perhaps arising from the detailed knowledge which the mining engineer already had. This was from Mr. Thomas Wilson who asked for a model of Hudgill Burn Mine because of litigation over interference by a neighbouring miner. It was being constructed in September 1844, also by Thomas Bewick, but there is no indication of its nature. Of Moel Wyn there is no mention.

One final mark of approval of the manner of constructing the large models should be made. It was the considered opinion by one admirer after a leisurely examination of one of the large models that it was "a work of sculpture and I think you have adopted the best method of obtaining the contours. I confess it would not have occurred to me, nor do I think I could improve upon it".[16] The opinion was not that of an engineer nor a geologist but of a sculptor, Sir Francis Chantrey.

The widespread admiration for the Dean Forest model and the gathering of so much geological talent for the meetings of the British Association in Newcastle in the summer of 1838 must have encouraged Sopwith to continue his efforts to display geological strata in model-form. On August 31st 1838 he records that Greenough, Smith and Buddle called at his office and afterwards met Barry, the architect, and de la Beche at the George Inn. Here Buddle, de la Beche and Sopwith arranged to make some geological and mining models. This seems to mark the beginning of plans to display more widely the fruits of mining activity which was one basis for the Museum of Economic Geology set up at the behest and under the control of de la Beche. It is contemporary with the determination by various parties to improve the national state of mining records, of which more later.

Geological strata had already been represented in block diagrams which emerged as models from the work of John Farey Senior (1766–1826). Farey's figures of stratified masses were produced in 1811 and have been described in some detail in a recent study.[17] In 1841 twenty-six models were given to the Geological Society of London by G.B. Greenough who had acknowledged Sopwith's help in the 2nd edition of the Geological map published in September 1840: twenty-two of these were model versions of Farey's block diagrams, there were two wedges and two unit blocks. It is not known when they were made but Greenough's own contribution to geological mapping, where William Smith had not been able to afford to publish more fully, kept Greenough alert to developments. Sopwith dined at Greenough's house in March 1839 and met John Farey junior at the Institute of Civil Engineers. When Sopwith read a paper at the meeting of the Geological Society on January 6th 1841 about the set of thirty models which he had just shown to the president of the society, William Buckland, discussion afterwards included comment by Greenough on Farey's models.*

The models produced from John Farey senior's block diagrams have not been dated: nor do we know who made them. It has been argued that the models show a knowledge of faulting beyond that understood in 1811, and reference is made to John Buddle's sections of strata in the Newcastle coalfield (1831) illustrating inclined normal faults which could be simulated using the wedges of strata in the Farey collection.[18] But it was Sopwith's models which were shown engraved for Lyell's second edition of *Elements of Geology* in 1841 and their construction was better finished than the Farey-derived models, as befitted the work of a cabinet-maker of distinction.

The journal has several references to the new idealised models which Sopwith produced in 1840, although he may have had earlier

* See above chapter 12

forms to hand when lecturing to students of engineering at Durham
in 1839. Perhaps it was the experience of the difficulties of
transporting large models or the need for further visual aids to
explain principles to his students which at last provoked him to
provide smaller models. The journal is specific. The entry for June
1st 1840 states that he had recently "conceived the idea that a series
of interesting and instructive models might be made to illustrate
several geological features".[19] He had a short time before writing
made more than twenty and sketches three of them in the diary.
The first public display of them was at the Cutlers' Hall, Sheffield.
Here at a meeting of the Geological and Polytechnic Society
Sopwith lectured at length on plans, sections and models, exhibiting the small geological models.[20] In October 1840 some small
models had been made for Dr Buckland and sent off to Drayton
Manor where the recipient was a guest of Sir Robert Peel. Sopwith
was planning a set of about 40 and spent Christmas morning on the
project. He chose an able assistant named Liddle to construct them,
commenting that it was Buckland's commendation which had led
to making the models. The first January meeting of the Geological
Society was the ideal moment to launch a description of them.
Buckland was president of the society and Greenough was there to
comment on the improvement they represented over the Farey
designs. On January 12th the Institution of Civil Engineers was the
scene of a long proposal for preserving railway sections and a
chance to exhibit the models again. By March 1841 twelve had
been chosen with Buckland's advice.

"The beginner may find it by no means easy to understand such
copies," wrote Sir Charles Lyell in his 1841 edition of the *Elements
of Geology* of the pictures of the models chosen for his work,
"although if he were to examine and handle the originals, turning
them about in different ways, he would at once comprehend their
meaning . . .". Similarly to appreciate the nature of the small
models it is necessary to handle them, feel the solidity and admire
the grain and finish of aesthetically pleasing works of art. The

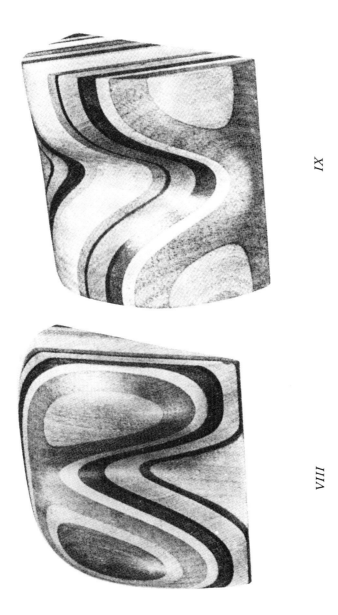

IX

VIII

Models VIII and IX of 1841 set.

construction of them has been revealed by the remarkable survival at the Hancock museum in Newcastle of working drawings.[21] Twenty-seven separate layers of wood were glued together in a prescribed order, varying from $\frac{3}{32}$ to $\frac{1}{2}$ inch, using satinwood, rosewood and ebony. Three inch lengths were sawn off the laminated block and appropriate sawing instructions marked on the drawings. The skill and economy which characterises the creation of these models adds to their merit, but the important features were stated by their author in a published description to go with sets of six or twelve models. The description, with lithograph drawings of all twelve models, could be usefully bought with the more elementary basic six models. "They are constructed," he wrote, "of various kinds of wood fitted together from actual measurements of the strata in the Coal and Leadmining districts of the North of England. The upper part of each model represents the surface of the ground, the sides exhibit four vertical sections usually drawn in geological works, and the base of each model represents a horizontal plane at a certain depth under the surface". These obvious statements emphasise the great advantage of viewing strata on one model without numerous perspective drawings. If the intersections of mineral veins and the effects of faulting are also shown, the advantage of a model becomes even more striking. Add to that the slicing in two of the model across an inclined plane and the illustration of twenty-four configurations of strata – both horizontal and inclined, with and without normal faulting – becomes possible from twelve models.

A set of twelve small models, four-inch not three-inch in this instance, was duly presented to the Geological Society of London on May 19th 1841 after the Club dinner presided over by Professor Whewell. On June 22nd, after time at the Polytechnic exhibition in London and seeing the royal procession for the proroguing of parliament, Sopwith had dinner with William Cubitt in Great George Street before going to the Institution of Civil Engineers. Here Buckland, Fairbairn of Manchester, Sir Mark Brunel and

Dr Reid, engineer for the ventilation of the Houses of Parliament, were amongst those present to hear the paper "on the construction and use of geological models in connection with civil engineering". The journal entry gives a list of the maps, plans, sections and models which were used to illustrate the paper. There were two Dean Forest models and slides of wood with the lime wood filling to show the mode of construction, a model of France by Schuster and two series of models, the set of twelve (presumably four-inch) and a series of fifteen small models, probably the three-inch version.[22] The minutes of the proceedings of the Institution of Civil Engineers also mention that Sopwith alluded to T.B. Jordan's model of the Dolcoath mine, housed in the Museum of Economic Geology. As well as commenting that the set of twelve models consisted of 579 pieces of wood, it was noted that one model had no less than 130 separate pieces. It is not surprising that the costs of making the models and the charge that was made for them discouraged students from acquisition of their own sets. J. Tennant of the Strand sold the set of six 3-inch models for £2, the description being a further 3 shillings. A set of twelve, 4-inch models cost £5. Tennant had sold £100 worth in the first year. They were not mass-produced, did require a high level of skill to make and were highly durable. In 1842 the Institution of Civil Engineers awarded their creator the Telford Silver Medal. This was a proud moment of recognition to receive a medal commemorating the great engineer who had himself proposed Sopwith's membership in 1833. Further recognition came from Murchison who took a set of models with him to Russia and finally from two princes. Buckland showed them to Prince Albert, the Prince Consort, on May 5 1842: on May 26th 1844 a set was presented to King Leopold of the Belgians and finally, on March 8th 1845, Sopwith was introduced to His Royal Highness Prince Albert at the Marquis of Northampton's soirée. The models and the survey of the Duchy of Cornwall mines which had been made by Sopwith were subjects of conversation and a little royal name-dropping concerning the king of the Belgians' interest in the mineral wealth of his kingdom also occurred. Even the satisfied geologist was suitably dazzled by "so rich a treat to a party nearly five hundred in number and comprising as much probably of the united aristocracies of rank, wealth and talent as could be found in any assemblage throughout the world".[23]

Two further subjects arose from the combined interests of mining and geology which had brought Sopwith to the forefront of public attention in these fields: these were the subjects of mining records and the Museum of Economic Geology. The keeping of accurate records by means of plans, sections and even models was dear to Sopwith's heart from his early years at Alston, reflected in his Hudgill mining plans. Expertise in mining might also be improved by the establishment of mining schools, a subject which is mentioned in the journal in May 1837 in connection with the possibility of such a school at Durham. The Polytechnic school in Cornwall promoted by Dr Davies Gilbert and Sir Charles Lemon was already in action by that time, providing an early example of the collection of information and dissemination by instruction notable in literary and philosophical societies but developing in more practical ways. On the matter of mining records Sopwith delivered himself at the most appropriate moment, namely at the British Association for the Advancement of Science meetings at Newcastle in August 1838.*

The first "Observations on the practicability and importance of preserving National Mining Records" written by him were set down on paper on August 13th. Comparison with Austrian methods were drawn as he made notes from Count Breunner's description of the Austrian Schools of Mines and their preservation of mining plans and records. As already mentioned the important committee was formed but there was no time for Sopwith to read his 'Observations' to the Geological Section of the BAAS. In November Buckland

---

*   See above chapter 12

had a printed paper before him outlining Sopwith's 'Observations'. Buckland was hoping that the Committee could convene in London to receive Sir Charles Lemon's report of his interview with Spring Rice, the Chancellor of the Exchequer. Buckland also mentioned de la Beche's collection of models and machines housed temporarily at Craig Court near Charing Cross. A better place would soon be procured and there ought to be a deposit room for records of mining too.

A better place and a new name was provided for the Museum which became known as the Museum of Practical Geology. Sopwith's concern and eye for publicity combined to forward the purpose of the Museum and the keeping of mining records which could be represented in documentary or model form. So it was that he published an "Account of the Museum of Economic Geology and Mining Records Office in 1843". The origins of the Museum lay in de la Beche's submission to the Chancellor of the Exchequer requesting that the work of the geological survey, examples of specimens collected, and the mapping and recording of these, might be gathered under one roof. The Office of Woods and Forests gave the go-ahead in 1837. De la Beche appointed Professor Richard Phillips as curator and T.B. Jordan, the Cornish engineer, as keeper of Mining Records. Phillips was a chemist and a laboratory for soil analysis was attached to the room housing the collection. Jordan was also a good instrument maker, knowledgeable about astronomy. The little volume alluded to numerous minerals, models and publications, not least to Sopwith's own although not to his surveying instruments. Cornish and Northumbrian examples predominated and the economic usefulness of such work as the stone commission for the re-building of the Houses of Parliament also featured, as well as the work of the Railway sections committee. The desirability of preserving railway sections had been discussed at the BAAS meeting at Glasgow in 1839. A committee chaired by Lord Northampton included de la Beche, Vignoles and Sopwith.

The museum became another place to visit with friends and occasional reference is made to approval of it by geologists, engineers and other acquaintances. It was a show place for much of Sopwith's achievement and a reminder that mining was the foremost activity to gain from studies in economic or practical geology. John Buddle and Sopwith met Leonard Horner of the Factory and Children's Employment Commissioners in April 1842, talking at length on the 1842 report with its famous wood engravings. Horner believed that these illustrations in the report would make a strong impression on the public. Despite such advances and regulation concerning the workforce, it was clear that progress was sadly slow as was evidenced in Sopwith's last major contribution on the subject of mining records in 1844.

The National Importance of Preserving Mining Records was dedicated to an old friend, Sir Charles Lemon, whose benevolence in offering up to £20,000 for a national school of mines had not been matched by government effort. The tract arose from a meeting of the Natural History Society of Newcastle-upon-Tyne chaired by Thomas Sopwith at which it was resolved "that a general and uniform registration of Mining Operations throughout the kingdom would tend to prevent many fatal accidents; would in other respects be of eminent utility to the interests of all persons concerned in mines; and would also confer a great national benefit". A bill would be drafted for the House of Commons by William Bainbridge. The pamphlet gave a fifty year review of the pressure to do something about the subject. William Thomas of Newcastle at a meeting of the Literary and Philosophical Society in 1797 had stated the need and in 1815 William Chapman cited Thomas after an accident near Newcastle had killed 75 miners where wastes had been left unrecorded, becoming filled with water or dangerous gases. Werner and Sopwith himself, urged by John Buddle to improve plans in the isometric drawing studies of 1834 and encouraged by John Taylor too, sought to provide a fuller record at a time when lead mining was too much of a mere lottery. It was necessary now to collect all existing plans and details of subterranean work and aim for uniform symbols and colours. Allusion was again made to the author's efforts in the Holyfield and Hudgill plan; to the Dean Forest work; to the committee arising out of the British Association meeting of 1838; to the Museum of Economic Geology and Buckland's establishment of a Mineral Records office in 1840–1.[*] And yet still there was "no material progress . . . towards regular, systematic and permanent record of the mining operations of these kingdoms".[24] Finally the pamphlet urged the authorities to look at Austro-Hungarian education of mining directors; Vandermaelen's able work in Belgium, naming and detailing mining operations for coal and iron; Phillips' own findings in the Museum's Laboratory and the work of Thomas Richardson in Newcastle, a pupil of the chemist Liebig; and the munificent patronage offered by Sir Charles Lemon for a mining school.

The effect of all this can only be guessed. Like many resolutions and tracts it may have had a slight currency and fallen largely on deaf ears. It may suggest that for all Sopwith's belief in himself he did not have the powers of persuasion needed to move governments. Not many men have. Whig reforms and Peelite improvements had shaken and re-shaped many institutions, but in the 1840s governments hovered between more regulation and less regulation as free trade became a reality and the complacency symbolised in part by the Great Exhibition of 1851 drew nearer. These were the years when more of the same would seem to be good enough: more iron for yet more railways but no need yet for steel from new methods; more coal for more steampower but few to stop and ask the human cost.

Effective or not, Sopwith's authorship was a further expression for an intense concern for orderliness and good sense in the fields in which he had become a professional expert. Meanwhile his own

---

[*]   Mine geological plans showing details of location and level along with very detailed geological information were drawn up for the Allenheads Lead Mine about 1845 (Mining Record Office – plan no 3608.)

professional work had taken on an international character as he crossed the channel and made his mark in the Sambre and Meuse coalfield of Belgium.

Chapter 15

Surveyor Abroad

"I rose at 5 o'clock and after placing a few travelling requisites in a small carpet bag I started at 6 in the *Water-Witch* steamboat for Boulogne".[1] For the first time Thomas Sopwith was leaving the British Isles and his love of travel to different places is reflected in the thorough details which he gives in his journal. He was now off to fulfil a large contract and as usual made good use of the time; observing foreign customs, enlarging his experience and recording much that was trivial, his enjoyment of life continued in new fields.

The purpose of the visit across the channel was a major survey in association with William Cubitt. The area to be surveyed was the district between the Sambre and Meuse rivers to assess the mineral capacity of the region and to propose the building of a railway to serve it and to exploit the minerals. Two months of strenuous work led to a full report and many interviews with prominent citizens in the autumn of 1843, with a further visit in 1844.

Preparations for his journey are briefly referred to in the journal. Getting a passport was a matter of visiting the Belgian embassy at 50 Portland Place and writing the application in a book: name, residence, place of birth, age, height and profession were entered and a passport was promised the following day. However when Sopwith mentioned that his business related to Belgian railways, a passport was produced at once. He went off to buy a velvet nap hat at Lincoln and Bennett's and after several unsatisfied calls because people were away from London in August, he talked about the proposed work with Cubitt and collected instructions from Mr.

Fearon. There were still more of these to come so he was delayed at Folkestone which gave him an opportunity to view Cubitt's work on the Folkestone to Dover railway line with its half-made tunnels.

The journey is only briefly described with details of the steam engine output and the dreary cabin of the *Water-Witch*. As the continental coast came into focus he noticed red-tiled houses and several working windmills past Cap Gris Nez and the approach to Boulogne was marked by ruins of Napoleon's forts built to defend his intended invasion force. At the quay military-looking customs officers took charge of the bags and Sopwith gave his key to the commissionaire for the Hotel du Nord. He did not appear to have his passport but gave details to an official without paying a further fee. Breakfast at the Hotel du Nord was a distressing affair – hurried, with dirty cutlery, cracked cups and crazy coffee pots with unpleasant contents. Dinner was rather better but clearly catering for the large number of British who passed through the town. A great deal of inquisitive sight-seeing was achieved before he re-turned, without explanation in the diary, to Dover. There was quite a rough crossing and most people appear to have succumbed to sea-sickness but not Sopwith who rather enjoyed the voyage. A summons to London from Mr. Fearon followed a pleasant couple of days at Cubitt's where the latter's microscope and telescopes, one trained on Boulogne and one on Jupiter and Saturn, gave happy diversion.

It was not until August 31st that progress to the continent again occurred. The journey was on the steamer *Soho* from Blackwall in the Thames. He left at 12.55 p.m. and thoroughly enjoyed his journey, being reluctant to leave the comfort of the steamer at Antwerp at 8.30 a.m. the next day. The customs men were "not a little bothered with my boxes of geological models"[2] but he did not have to pay duty on the two boxed sets of twelve each, nor on the maps for the survey. His host, Mr. Piddington, had time to take him to see the Jesuits' church before sitting down to drink some delicious lemonade, looking on at soldiers and officers enjoying iced water, sugar or lemonade over a game of dominoes, a game in England "for foreigners and children".[3] At midday he followed Captain Pernez of the Corps of Engineers into the citadel where in a cool, comfortable office they took their coats off and began to examine the plans, sections and working drawings of the Sambre and Meuse railway done under Pernez' direction. Refreshing draughts of champagne kept them going until 4 p.m. A few glasses of Bordeaux with M. Antoine Verborg, an interested party, preceded a journey by third class wagon to Malines, the centre of the Belgian railway system. He continued to Brussels where he retired to bed well pleased in the Hotel d'Europe at 10 p.m., nearly eighteen hours after he had got up to follow on a Vandermaelen map the journey along the Scheldt.

While in Brussels there were introductions for the surveyor to government officials and to the music festival at Louvain where the composer Limnander obtained some seats for Sopwith, Piddington and the latter's little girls Elizabeth and Rose. On September 4th he called on a newspaper editor who was also a director of the Museum of Industry in Brussels where he presented one of his sets of geological models. A letter of introduction from John Walker the London mapmaker was given to Mr. P. Vandermaelen and he came away with a present of some valuable maps. Later he admired the Museum of Industry at greater length and wrote of it with enthusiasm. When Mr. Piddington sprained an ankle and stayed in his room communications were a little harder. Sopwith comments with surprise that English was little known, "certainly very much less than French is spoken and read in England". He found his Belgium companions patient and polite at his efforts to speak French.

The real work started on September 7th. In company with Piddington and Pernez, a distance of 24 miles was walked from near Charleroi, mostly on the actual line of the railway. "Every rock, every village and every change of view interested me and aided by good maps I soon acquired a correct notion of the geological structure of the country".[4] The next day was very hot and it was regretted that a carriage was not available on the road sections. The last four miles by turnpike walking into the sun towards Philippeville were described as very oppressive. A cabriolet was therefore hired for the day from Mariemburg on September 9th: a pre-breakfast excursion to Couvin ironworks and a large breakfast of various meats, fish, Bordeaux wine and Burgundy and ale was the prelude to another cloudless day. The heat made a change of clothing necessary for the ensuing days so that Sopwith preferred "a broad-brimmed straw hat, a pair of thin linen trousers, no waistcoat, no stock or neckcloth and a thin linen blouse or loose frock coat". He also carried a black leather wallet over his shoulder for his note and sketchbooks.[5] Time was short because Pernez only had a few days leave of absence but conveyances or horses do not seem to have been readily available. Nevertheless cheerful entries in the diary state that the limestone scenery was much admired and comparisons were made with Alston as to the occurrence of lead veins. Hotels and even small country inns seem to have been wonderfully clean and the frequent appearance of marble used for quite humble dwellings caught his attention.

Arguments about travel disturbed Sopwith's rest early on the morning of September 10th. Six good reasons for not using the public diligence leaving for Dinant at 4 a.m. were given in the journal – the dark, the inability to stop when necessary, the lack of space to spread out maps and the chatter of other passengers were enough to make him grumble at the prospect. Fortunately Piddington persuaded Pernez that a voiture and pair of horses would be much more suitable and after three arduous days it did seem more reasonable: the Givet to Dinant drive was a pleasure after all.

An independent frame of mind was still evident over the question of progressing to Namur. Pernez intended to go in the evening of September 10th but Sopwith realised that the banks of the Meuse from Dinant to Namur provided the geological key to the district. Quite apart from that the state of river navigation was an important

factor when considering a bridge for the railway. Pernez spent the
evening with friends while Sopwith studied his maps. He was glad
to view the district by daylight the next day. Writing up his report
and a visit to M. Magis, government engineer, kept him busy the
day after but he had time to relax at the Philharmonic and Literary
Society too. The band played and he noticed that beer glasses were
provided with tin covers to keep the flies out. He was glad to see
that the Mons newspaper lying on a table there had an article on
"the learned engineer Sopwith".

In mid-September a visit was paid to the field of Waterloo which
stirred romantic and proud reflections. Back at Charleroi he received a copy of the *Newcastle Journal* on September 30th which
told him of the birth of his son Arthur, a letter with the same news
having not reached him. A bottle of champagne was added to the
evening meal. The first week of October was spent at Charleroi
before going to Mons where a French newspaper gave him the
melancholy news of the death of G.W. Wood M.P. of Manchester
at a meeting of the Manchester geological society. His new acquaintances at Mons were Guillemin, geologist, and Ponson who
was writing an elaborate work on mining. Pernez arrived for a
second spell on October 10th and the survey began again the next
day. Quarries of red marble and of slate were viewed and October
13th was a long day, starting at 5.30 a.m. and finishing with
Sopwith helping the driver of the voiture find his way in the dark
with the aid of the surveyor's maps. The rather hurried notes of
October 14th to 22nd include little about the survey and barely
describe the scenery but he was ready to return to Ostend and cross
the channel to London by October 28th. He was deeply shocked to
hear of John Buddle's death from Sir James Duke whom he met
on the journey. Buddle had been a great supporter as well as a
valued friend and companion in the Dean Forest work.

The pace of work continued back at home: the Health of Towns
committee in Newcastle, an enquiry concerning the Newcastle and
Carlisle railway and a report on the Norton Hill mine in Somerset

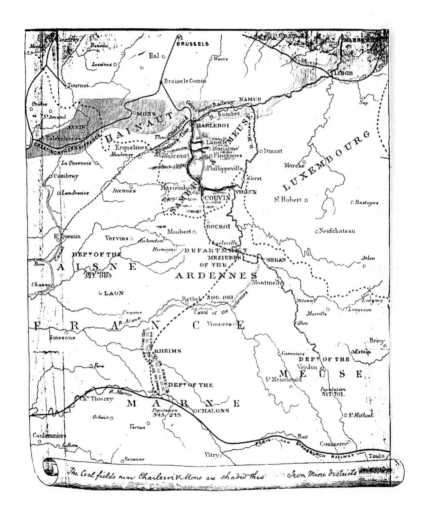

Sambre and Meuse District in 1845.

on behalf of the Dean and Chapter of Christ Church, Oxford all occupied him. He wrote a memoir on Buddle and another on J.C. Loudon a much admired friend who had died on December 14th. Meanwhile there were plans to send his eldest boy Jacob, son by his first beloved wife, to school in Brussels. This proved not to be a success despite early encouragement: the unhappy Jacob ran away and when he later joined the army and went to India, largely with his father's blessing, he died at the age of only nineteen.

A second visit to the continent took place in February 1844 after a journey in a private train from London to Folkestone on the South-Eastern railway line of which Mr. Baxendale, head of Pickfords the carriers, was chairman, and Cubitt the chief engineer. The three of them took the steamer from Dover to Ostend, going on to Bruges, Ghent and Brussels. There was some re-covering of ground for the benefit of Cubitt but new work was in hand at the end of the month and on March 5th at 8.30 a.m. they were received at an audience at the Palace of Laaken by King Leopold. This lasted for half an hour and consisted of questions about the Sambre-Meuse railway and flattering comments about the English character, not least about Cubitt himself.

Much of the visit to Belgium consisted in showing Cubitt the work which Sopwith had already done before they extended the survey together. The diarist excuses himself from writing at greater length, merely repeating with some explanation the notes he wrote probably in the type of notebook mentioned in an earlier chapter.[*] As the entries are being transcribed in November 1876, they lose something of the freshness of the original record. The return journey took the travellers to Calais from where they caught the *Widgeon* steampacket to Dover. From there they went to view the double tunnel on the Dover-Folkestone railway, completed but not yet open to the public. Sopwith, using a small hand telescope, observed that something was coming towards them in the tunnel

---

[*] See above chapter 13.

which would collide with the low flat car or lorry on which Cubitt and he were being conveyed. Despite Cubitt's assurance that this was impossible and strictly against his orders, another vehicle was indeed approaching but fortunately stopped. Cubitt duly chastened the assistant engineer on the offending wagon which had to retreat before the progress of the lorry bearing the chief engineer.

Late in March Sopwith was busy writing up the report of the Sambre-Meuse survey while living in London. He visited the Belgium ambassador, Van de Weyer, on March 19th amongst many other calls to old friends and acquaintances such as Mrs Loudon, Edwin Chadwick and Rowland Hill of penny post fame. By April 10th the proof sheets for the report on the Sambre-Meuse railway were ready. Back in Newcastle he was still working on the map for the railway giving instructions on its colouring. On April 25th he travelled to London and was having further discussions with the promoters of the Sambre and Meuse railway as well as showing Colonel de Puydt, Mrs Riche and Mr. Piddington the wonders of Clegg's atmospheric railway and the majesty of Windsor Castle. The provisional contract for the Sambre-Meuse railway being now signed, Sopwith and the engineer Anderson were off again to Brussels. Here an interview with the Minister of Public Works took place and another, of four hours, with the government Inspector of Railways. He also saw his son Jacob at school. After pressing his views strongly on the tariff for the new railway and apparently persuading the Belgians that the English providers of capital funds had certain prerequisites, Sopwith suggested that a further interview with King Leopold might satisfy the English parties to the railway business.

A further interview with royalty undoubtedly suited Sopwith too but he was nonetheless most impressed by the King's understanding of the business: the extension to Sedan, the unreliable navigation of the Meuse in winter flood or in summer drought, the huge but barely tapped resources of coal, iron, marble and slate were all discussed. Mention of the Dinant marbles was the cue for

Sopwith to present a copy of his *Account of the Museum of Economic Geology*: specimens of the marbles had already been placed at the museum after Sopwith's earlier visit. A perusal of the book led on to the subject of geological models and a set was offered to the King. Sopwith waxed enthusiastic over the advantages of foreign enterprise, the spread of capital, the sharing of scientific research, the development of natural resources and the peace and prosperity of nations. "Mr. Anderson joined from time to time in the conversation", we are told.[6] It was altogether a most satisfactory audience.

The first stages of the work in Belgium were more or less complete. A general exhortation to young Jacob to improve his writing and to work hard was made on May 26th, the day of the royal interview. Was the father too ambitious for the son? Relations did not improve thereafter as far as we can tell. Meanwhile Anderson and Sopwith found themselves on opposite sides of a courtyard at the Hotel de Flanders so they rigged up a continuous string ropeway between their windows to enable a fifteen second delivery of messages, papers etc. and to avoid having to go up and down two staircases and walk the length of a gallery. On June 12th they left Brussels and caught the *Antwerpen* steam boat. An unfortunate accident marred the voyage when the stern of a fishing boat was stove in by the *Antwerpen*. Two boys were drowned as the fishing boat went down: two fishermen were saved, brought on board and received a sympathetic subscription before being put off at Gravesend where they lived. London business was soon occupying Sopwith again – a commission to settled disputes concerning the Duchy of Cornwall was uppermost – and a copy of the report of the Sambre and Meuse railway was taken by Dr Buckland and given to Sir Robert Peel. On June 18th the directors of the Sambre and Meuse agreed to fall in with Sopwith's request for 100 Sambre and Meuse shares paid up to £6 per share as remuneration for his work that year.

A further chapter in business abroad was soon to open up.

Meanwhile in the autumn of 1844 his loyalties were a little stretched for he was interested in helping Brunnel with plans to promote an atmospheric railway through Northumberland to Scotland. This was in direct competition with George Stephenson who wondered what Brunel was doing north of the Tyne anyway. Sopwith was amused when Stephenson added playful intimidation to his question and seized Brunel by the collar. However Stephenson grumbled to his friends about Brunel's plans and later gave Sopwith a similar collar-shaking when he dared to suggest that a Stephenson viaduct had affected some property of Sopwith's by almost blocking up windows and preventing a free circulation of air. "Now Sopwith – if ever I hear you speak such d . . . d nonsense again – I'll never speak to you more".[7] In the event friendship was maintained, for Sopwith not only travelled with George Stephenson along with Hudson, the York-based railway king, on November 17 but also accompanied the great engineer to Brussels and partook of the dinner given to George Stephenson as will be seen. The friendship with Stephenson's son Robert was much closer and later Robert and Sopwith travelled to Egypt to see the railway designed by Robert Stephenson. Samuel Smiles' *Life of George and Robert Stephenson* makes it plain that the mutual respect of Robert and Thomas was cemented not least in the depositions made on the question of the safety lamp which George Stephenson constructed in 1817, less well-known but contemporary with the better-known example made by Humphry Davy.

The post of commissioner to hear disputes arising from the Duchy of Cornwall's operations did not come Sopwith's way after all. The journal gives a copy of Sir Charles Lemon's letter regretting that the appointment did not fall to him. In the autumn there were family strains. Jacob wrote to say that he had left school and come to London. His anxious father took the train to London to be told that someone like Jacob had taken the steamship to Newcastle. It was not Jacob and a second journey to London was necessary. Scotland Yard was informed and Jacob was traced to the Isle of

Wight, having enlisted. A painful interview ensued during which Jacob fainted. The effect on Jane who had rheumatism was also most distressing. Sopwith as usual drove himself on in his regular business, his accustomed reaction to family sorrow. There was plenty of business too for the huge quantity of work in the surveying and building of railways was being delayed by lack of engravers in late November. On Thursday November 28th, having already covered twenty-five miles by cab looking for engravers of plans, he got to bed at 3 a.m. Up again at 7 a.m. he travelled another fifty miles on Thursday and thirty miles on Friday placing and collecting the work.[8]

There was plenty more work in the new year locally, in Nottinghamshire, in Swansea and up in London again. Brunel and Sopwith were to act as arbitrators in some surveying business concerning Lord Caernarvon's property. Grainger was up in town and went with him to Greenwich and was also shown Truman's Brewery, a frequent port of call. Recently made a Fellow of the Society of Arts Sopwith also took W.G. Armstrong to a soirée at Lord Northampton's as well as going to Allison's Manufactory to see Armstrong buy a piano. At last it was time for Stephenson, Fearon and Sopwith together with his assistant Benjamin Scott to leave once more for Ostend and Brussels. The director of the Traffic department of the Government lines of railway was keen to find a place for his son on the Sambre and Meuse railway and so visited Sopwith. Acquaintance was renewed with the Piddington children and on March 25th 1845, Stephenson, Sopwith and two others began their viewing of the countryside along the route of the railway between the Sambre and the Meuse. One place for staying the night was at Namur where the Hotel de Harscamp stood close to a clock tower which emitted sonorous notes loudly for about 330 times both early in the morning, at 4 a.m. or 5 a.m. and at 9 p.m. and 11 p.m. The striking took close on fifteen minutes. Sopwith appreciated the sound and commented that it was a pity that a decent hotel should be avoided because Murray's handbook of Belgium warned the intending visitor of the bell.

All the while he was getting to know George Stephenson who dwelt upon his earlier days – ploughing for 2 pence a day and breakfast, suffering the twelve hours toil in the engine house as well as mending clocks and watches in the evenings and of course designing and building the *Rocket* locomotive. Perhaps more to the point Sopwith was renewing acquaintance with Belgian engineers and in one instance meeting one in error, on April Fool's day too, he remarks, mistaking his recollection of M. Guillemin and seizing on the name of M. Gonot. M. Gonot was not in the least put out, answering an invitation to dine and proving a useful source of information. This was all the more remarkable in so far as despite Gonot's professional reputation, Sopwith had in fact criticised his report and he might therefore have been somewhat cool towards the Englishman.[9] Fortunately the chief engineer of the Belgian Mines not only dined but remained friendly and helpful over the succeeding days, accompanying the travellers to the Jemappes collieries where they viewed the pit engines, going by canal to the coke ovens and completing a pleasant day taking wine with M. Gonot.

One of the main purposes of the trip took place on April 4th: a banquet was given by the Engineers of Belgium to George Stephenson. It was in a Brussels restaurant where Belgian and English flags were surmounted by a union jack, surrounding a marble pedestal on which the bust of George Stephenson rested, crowned with laurels. The table decoration was dominated by an archway with a model of the *Rocket* locomotive. M. Massui, Chief Director of the Belgian railways, presided, Stephenson at his right hand and Sopwith at his left. There were about forty other diners, many connected with railway management, and an excellent evening was enjoyed. A copy of the menu is stuck into the diary a few pages further on. No other details are given however and there is a relatively brief entry referring to a private audience with King Leopold.

Stephenson illustrated the geology of the country amusingly[*] while his Majesty discoursed on the trade cycle. He did not forget to thank Sopwith for his models, stating that much time must have been taken to devise them. The royal handshake and, "I wish you success in all your undertakings", was a fitting completion of the visit.

It was not quite the last visit on business for an urgent call by Mr. Fearon to go to Belgium yet again led to a further journey there on April 16th 1845. The Ostend steam packet captain was not sanguine of him reaching his destination from Dover in the storm which had beaten up and indeed it was learned later that the journey took twenty-four hours instead of five or six. Calais was also too exposed so Sopwith went to Boulogne in the *Charon*. "The sea was very high but I sat on deck all the voyage with a rope round my waist (being often lifted from my seat by the violent motion of the boat) and as I am exempt from sea-sickness[†10] I greatly enjoyed the sublime spectacle of the rolling waves".[11] Even at Boulogne the packet had to wait and the final part of the journey was very hazardous. A pilot boat approached to take off the mails and any passengers prepared to risk it: two others joined Sopwith and jumped down into the pilot boat, which negotiated the sand bar under full sail, passing through dangerous breakers and grazing on the sand several times before grounding in calmer water near the pier. A small boat collected mail and passengers after nothing worse than a drenching. The seventeen hour journey to Lille was an opportunity for sleep with occasional views in waking moments.

---

[*] Samuel Smiles wrote in his *Lives of the Engineers: George and Robert Stephenson* that Stephenson used his own hat as part of his demonstration and then remarked to his companion as they came away, "By the bye, Sopwith, I was afraid the King would see the inside of my hat; it's a shocking bad one!". The journal does not unfortunately corroborate the story but perhaps Sopwith communicated it to Smiles at a later date.

[†] This is not wholly accurate. He had succumbed in the Bristol channel on February 13th but in his own footnote states "very slightly and not genuine sea-sickness".

The railway took him from there to Brussels and interviews followed in the evening of April 17th and on the morning of the 18th with the secretary and the Minister of Public works respectively. The project was the West Flanders railways. Sopwith did not approve of what he saw and drew up new arrangements with an eye not only to the service of all the important towns but also to local convenience and further extension. The Minister, M. Deschamps, duly recommended these plans in a three hour interview to a deputation from Bruges led by the Governor of West Flanders. The convention was signed after a slightly prolonged stay because of a cabinet meeting to which the Minister of Public Works had to be called away. Sopwith was anxious to be back in London for parliamentary business. Belgian affairs seem to have been accomplished remarkably expeditiously.

The sudden departure on this last business to Belgium was perhaps the final straw for Jane. Although Thomas had done his best to make her feel at home and show her the sights of London, he had already interrupted that pleasure to work on railway business before Fearon's note had summoned him to go to Belgium. It was an exceptionally busy time in the midst of the railway mania. George Stephenson had travelled to the north of Spain to advise on a railway scheme there as well as approving of Sopwith's West Flanders' work. It was a trip which severely affected George's health. Robert Stephenson's engineering works would take him to Canada and Egypt, fortified by narcotics but ultimately wearing him out despite partial retirement. Brunel, like Robert Stephenson, would also die prematurely aged in his fifties. Whether Jane foresaw illness and exhaustion or not, she had no desire to keep pace with London nor continental life. She was thankful that her husband had accepted a new post by the end of the year which required him to return and live in Northumberland.

Chapter 16

1845 – a Turning Point

The year 1845 is no different from those immediately preceding it for the successful mining engineer. The range of work and interests does not pall for one who was a seasoned traveller and incipient cosmopolitan, working in London more frequently and not unfamiliar with Brussels. Opportunities were legion in both mining and railway developments at home and abroad. To professional status could be added a wide circle of friends and clients in the metropolis and across the kingdom. Yet in 1845, much to the dismay of many of these friends, Sopwith's career took a different turn. He largely gave up new national and international work and took on the job of chief agent to the WB lead mines in Allendale. To some this change marked departure into obscurity. That was not Sopwith's view.

The exact circumstances of the new appointment are by no means clear. The conditions which the recipient requested were evidently important and became more so when they were threatened at a later date. On February 28th 1845 Armorer Donkin called on Sopwith at Newcastle and "stated that the period had arrived for some further and immediate progress in the matter of an appointment in which I am much interested". This may have been the appointment to the agency in Allendale but there were other Northern developments. It is significant that on March 4th he was at Spency Croft, Alston at a meeting of the Roughtengill Mining Company which declared a dividend of 250 per cent for the year. Such wealth undoubtedly helped to persuade him that lead-mining in the Pennines remained profitable. On May 20th "I called on Mr.

Atkinson at half past eleven and walked with him through the parks to the residence of Mr. Beaumont in Piccadilly Terrace. I had an interview of some length with that gentleman which resulted in a cordial and entire reception of the views mutually entertained with reference to an appointment in Mr. Beaumont's service at some future period. Mr. Atkinson and Mr. Beaumont were made acquainted with all the details of my present occupations and engagement and the explanations were of the most full and candid description"[1] This then marked the start of a new career which bore fruit for employer and agent alike, although not without its disagreements and misunderstandings.

The journal contains an interesting memorandum at this point.[2] The immediately preceding material of May 1845 was written up in July 1845. The memorandum was written nearly twenty-two years later in April 1867. From mid June 1845 the material was written up in 1876 and in most of the subsequent volumes, referring to the events of 1845 to 1854, the material was written up in 1876 and 1877. The diaries or notebooks were usually brief but of sufficient clarity for the author to write up their contents into the fuller Journal a few days, weeks or months later. That he does not trouble to write in great detail over thirty years later is not surprising, and since he was usually discreet in his journal it cannot be supposed that he omitted anything significant about his appointment or the later strains.*

Thomas Wentworth Beaumont was a landowner in Northumberland and Yorkshire whose mining interests in coal and lead made him a wealthy man. With houses at Bretton Hall, near Huddersfield, Bywell, near Stocksfield and in London, he could afford to engage a good agent for his interests. Later concern with Allendale developments suggests that the family retained a close interest for

---

* The chief problem arose over tenure of the house at Allenheads. One condition of the appointment was that the new chief agent should be allowed to build his own house which he did. Allenheads Hall was a fine house. Unfortunately Mr. Beaumont's wife Lady Margaret also thought so and wanted it for her own use.

the welfare and progress of the inhabitants of the dale urged on by the agent himself. In June 1845 however T.W. Beaumont was chiefly interested in finding a tutor for his eldest son. Dr Buckland recommended a Mr. Hughes which recommendation Beaumont was happy to take but would have liked to know whether Hughes was athletic and proficient in boating. As luck would have it Hughes was a guest of Mr. Richards, chairman of the Sambre and Meuse Company known to Sopwith. Richards' son and Hughes had both rowed for Oxford: G.E. Hughes (Rugby and Oriel) was president of boats in 1842 and E.V. Richards had rowed in the previous year. Sopwith was able to assure his new employer of Hughes' athletic prowess.

Part of the changing circumstances of working, but not more permanently living, in London led to the taking of new premises at no. 1 Chapel Place. Sopwith visited these on June 25th at the suggestion of Mr. T.M. Smith who had seen them advertised by Trollope, estate agents in Parliament Street. Smith proposed that they should make a contract the next day but Sopwith decided they had better do so there and then and, as they left the office, a disappointed applicant entered. Sopwith was still based in Norfolk Street when on July 1st he officially became Chief Agent of the W.B. Lead Mines. There were many years ahead of dealing with the firm Finlay, Hodgson & Co. which had looked after T.W. Beaumont's mining affairs and he records that he always found Mr. Hodgson an honourable, just, prudent and generous man.

At this point in the journal a review is made of past achievements and a justification made for the acceptance of a post which many felt to be inferior. The reflections were written in 1876 and may well be tinged with a glow added over the years. Nevertheless it is appropriate to consider the apologia and realise that far more than professional work was at stake. So in the journal it is stated first and foremost that the comfort of family and enjoyment of home "far exceeds all other views as to leave me no option".[3] The love and concern for Jane was expressed in the journal for 1831, now missing, quoted by Richardson. "The year 1831 will ever hold an honoured place in my memory, as having added greatly to my happiness by my union with a most esteemed and amiable girl, who has proved a most affectionate companion, a prudent manager of household affairs, and a most tender and diligent guardian of my dear boy . . . The event of next moment was my illness which for three months kept me from business and brought me to the verge of the grave. And here let me record with much affectionate regard the inestimable value of the constant and judicious attention of my dear wife, that if any of my posterity should hereafter read these pages they may, if she be living, honour and esteem her, and, if departed, may seek for grace to follow the good example she has shown". Jane was to die in 1855.

Sopwith admits that when the proposition was made to take the agency of the Beaumont mines he had gained "what I may fairly call a good position in my profession". The successes are then listed: surface and subterranean surveys at Alston and over much of central Northumberland; successful competition with McAdam over the Otterburn road; membership of the Institution of Civil Engineers; Commissioner in the Forest of Dean survey; surveys of passenger and colliery railways in the Newcastle region and recently much further afield; commissioner for the Coal Trade of the North of England. He did not forget to mention the enjoyment of the friendship of the northern historians Surtees and Hodgson, the kindness of Antony Hedley and the generosity of William Ord of Whitfield and Sir John Swinburne of Capheaton. He states that "in Railway Engineering I was among the very first who were largely employed in extensive and profitable surveys and in Lead Mining – the position of Chief Agent of all the three districts of Mines in Coalcleugh, Allendale and Weardale was undoubtedly the first position open to a professional person. The offer of it to me was at all events a great honour . . . "[4]

It was clear to Sopwith that his professional calling had taken him and would further take him from home very frequently, for weeks and even months. The prospect of moving his main offices to London was too much for Jane who disliked London for its effect both on her health and her domestic enjoyment. Brought up surrounded by sea and sand-dunes at Ross near Belford, she infinitely preferred the wide open spaces of Northumberland. A new house would be built for the family "with Gardens and open space for pleasure grounds for my children to play in. The prospect of comfort in the exercise of my duties at Home . . . the reasonable prospect of quietitude in the evening of life was pressed upon my attention".[5] It did not quite work out like that in practice: both wife and house were lost all too soon, but the prospect was indeed attractive in 1845. He could see it both at Donkin's and very soon at William Armstrong's, first in Jesmond Dene and later at Cragside on a truly grand scale.

Meanwhile adjustments connected with the new career and in adapting the old continued through the year. The Crawhall family had played a considerable part in the running of the Beaumont mines. William and George Crawhall resigned and retired respectively but Isaac Crawhall was retained in his position in Weardale. There were dealings with J.G. Atkinson too, the brother-in-law of T.W. Beaumont, and the journal explains for the first time that the mines in Allendale and Weardale were known as the W. B. mines from a former owner, William Blackett, a Yorkshire coal-owner. Further details emerge on August 23rd when W.G. Armstrong, still pursuing the profession of solicitor, called at the Sopwiths' house in St. Mary's Terrace, Newcastle with a deed of partnership between T.M. Smith and Marcus Scott (Jane Sopwith's brother, who had been working for her husband for some years) to take on all of Thomas' engineering business except his work for the crown and foreign contracts. Beaumont had agreed that one quarter of Sopwith's time each year, up to three months in aggregate, would be spent on work for the Commissioners of Woods and Forests or other business. Messrs Smith and Scott would be salaried and out of the remaining surplus Sopwith would receive one third share of the profits.

Allenheads Chapel.

By August 26th the new chief agent was ready to visit Allenheads in Allendale, calling on Mr. William Crawhall en route. The formal handing over of books took place, the names of assistants and clerks were noted and the plans of the mines transferred. Crawhall was allowed to stay on a few days: he was sad to leave after a very long association with Allendale, having received only a moderate salary but various perquisites. Sopwith disapproved of this "mode of recompence (sic)" in his own case and had negotiated totally different terms hoping to avoid any disputes over buying of stores or monopoly of labour. Crawhall fortunately did well out of Hudgillburn Mine and had his own property at Stagshaw: Sopwith had known him for twenty years and acted as arbitrator between Crawhall and the directors of the Newcastle and Carlisle railway in the past. The handover seems to have been cordial if sad. George Crawhall was visited on August 28th at Newhouse in Weardale but no details about work are given. Indeed Sopwith makes a point in his journal of explaining that he wished to be discreet about his professional business and although there is no hint of difficulty even in the summaries he makes thirty years after the event, it is possible that misgivings or misunderstandings arose even earlier than he subsequently states.

Jane's first visit to Allenheads was not encouraging. She, Thomas and his sister Mary Hindhaugh went by rail to Haydon Bridge and took a chaise to Allenheads. The house which would be the home of Thomas and Jane at first was seriously dilapidated. Before they left the head of the dale a dense fog descended. A few days later Thomas acquired some coach horses and a phaeton, the latter costing £65. On Saturday September 13th he, Jane and their daughter Emily arrived to take up residence. On Monday he received a deputation of Miners headed by Joseph Heslop, dissatisfied with the subsistence of 7/6* and he was soon visiting the various areas of mineral workings and dressing-floors.

---

* The miners received seven shillings and sixpence per week or thirty shillings per lunar month as a subsistence rate. They also made bargains to extract the ore and were paid quarterly.

The development of the new career is steadily unfolded in the remainder of 1845 and in subsequent months. The new house on which Thomas Sopwith put so much store was discussed with Mr. Nixon, Beaumont's land agent at Bywell. Details are given of other activities such as being 'Master of the Hounds' which meant following the hare on foot for most of the participants. He was glad to leave the details to Mr. Steel, the East Allendale Smelt Mills manager. Sopwith never shrank from the exercise but was perhaps happier setting up his telescope to observe Saturn and Jupiter than indulging in the rough pastimes of the chase. A meeting in London with T.W. Beaumont, after a visit to Harrow School and a presentation of *An Account of the Museum of Economic Geology* to the eldest son, Wentworth Blackett Beaumont, occurred on November 8th. The architect E.B. Lamb was there to discuss plans for the new house. It should not cost more than £4000, three-quarters of this on the hall itself and one quarter on the approaches, gardens and pleasure grounds to provide "a condition suitable for the comfort of my family".[6] One member of that family was still causing concern: Jacob was articled as a pupil in lead mining and other engineering business with a Mr. Eddy, apparently in the Dean Forest or Swansea area, but this effort to settle the eldest son was no more successful than previous plans.

Although Allenheads was becoming the centre of his life and work there was another visit abroad in November, this time to Paris in connection with a chancery suit. The journey from Southampton to Le Havre was very stormy but Sopwith as usual was able to enjoy breakfast and a dinner of roast beef while all the other passengers but one were sea-sick. Part of the journey, from Rouen to Paris, was by train, the diligence simply being taken off its wheels and placed on a frame with railway wheels. No account of his work follows but much of the time was spent with the Beaumonts who showed him round and let him use their carriage. Friendship was reciprocated when Sopwith showed them his telescope which he had set up in his rooms.

In late November the weather at Allenheads was wet and cold and on December 1st Mr. Lamb the architect arrived to look at the site of the hall and discuss other arrangements. The land agent Mr. Nixon came two days later and the site was fixed on the grounds of Craig house, described as "an old and ruinous hamlet partly inhabited but yet much dilapidated and the surface of the ground very uneven. There are however two very fine sycamore trees well worth preserving".[7] Emily and Arthur had now joined their parents staying in Allenheads and were probably impatient to see their home emerge. Mining business led to some dark and gloomy journeys over to Weardale but there were more serious forebodings of problems for the new chief agent, although he tackled them with a customary assurance which infuriated his opponents.

The two problems which arose concerned the pay and mutual aid for miners and secondly, objections from Mr. Isaac Crawhall. Very much aware of the hardships of the miner when trade was bad, the chief agent hoped that a system of mutual aid could be organised which would give some relief. Miners might have small-holdings or tiny garths to provide a little food and in some cases have more substantial agricultural activity to supplement the livelihood. What Sopwith regretted was the swift expenditure of hard-earned wages at the fairs with their attendant gambling and drinking, fairs which appeared at the time of the long pays on a quarterly basis and which quickly reduced the cash in hand. Fairs doubtless gave a cheerful draught of excitement but could easily leave bitter lees for the improvident. As early as 1846 Sopwith was issuing "observations" addressed to the miners and when an attempt was made in 1849 to enforce new contractual arrangements by which the miner had to keep to strict hours, a strike occurred. The new broom of efficiency smacked of meddlesome interference in the eyes of some: the eye of another, or that of his assistants, was clapped to the telescope and focussed upon the entrance to the mine at the agreed time of entry by the workforce! It is possible that the new style of management was rejected by Isaac Crawhall too. He may have felt threatened or may have been ignored. Certainly there were stresses and strains in the early days of the agency, but overall the new job was fulfilling and the new home joyfully realised.

* * *

The story of the achievements after 1845 is one of both continuity and difference. The professional man with wide scientific and artistic interests did not become isolated in a bleak Northumbrian dale. His influence on that dale* as well as that upon the West Allen and on Weardale was significant and his estimation of the task he was set was largely borne out by events. If the lead-mining industry of the northern Pennines would not long outlast his lifetime he could nevertheless enjoy vicariously the success of his second and third sons, Thomas and Arthur, in the mining of lead near Linares, central Spain and of coal on Cannock Chase, Staffordshire. Both benefited from a happy childhood at Allenheads Hall, enjoyment of the playground of the nearby burns†, being followed by apprenticeship with Armstrong at Elswick on the Tyne and in the coalmines of Durham before a wider experience of civil and mining engineering was learned in other continents. Their father continued his journal for another thirty-three years and there were other landmarks which pleased him – M.A. from Durham University, the Presidency of the Meteorological Society and numerous

---

*   The construction of the Blackett level, not an original idea, and incomplete, enabled the fuller exploitation of minerals, aided too by W.G. Armstrong's hydraulic engines.

†   There are two paintings executed by Clement Burlison in the 1850's. One shows Jane seated in the drawing-room of Allenheads Hall with her daughter Ursula and son Arthur respectively standing and kneeling by her. The second depicts the two boys, Tom and Arthur, turning up stones in a local burn and looking for fish while two family dogs look on: a pack train wends along a track over the head of the valley near the sky-line.

opportunities to enjoy new inventions and pursue his observations of them. After Jane's death in 1855 he was able to visit London more frequently again and continue friendships of many years standing, although inevitably the journal becomes a catalogue of their deaths too.

The difference after 1845 lay in a degree of self-appointed withdrawal which expressed itself just as powerfully but on a smaller canvas. The paternal instincts may at times have been too insistent for the lead miners of the dales of Allen and Wear but Thomas Sopwith was flexible enough as agent, though never squire, to provide education and encouragement to all who would respond. The tough life and harsh climate of the moors above Allenheads as well as hard conditions underground or in the crushing-mills were not new to him, but for one who had met with princes and sat at table with the great minds of science, it seems a strange choice to drive oneself so hard and be so distant from the spotlight. The answer lies perhaps in the happy concurrence of science and practical ability which were so ably combined in many Victorians and not least in the life of a fine Northumbrian geologist and engineer.

Appendix I

The Diary

The diary which Thomas Sopwith kept extended from October 1821 until January 1879 when he very deliberately brought it to a close. The first surviving volume dates from 1828 and in a memorandum apparently written at Allenheads in October 1855 it is recorded that a journal was begun in a regular and permanent form on 28 October 1821. It was written in a large account book and covered the period 28 October 1821 to 2 June 1823. These were years during which he was employed at his father's workshops. In the evenings he entered details of his occupations or observations. "These were of necessity trivial yet I found not only pleasure but advantage in keeping such a journal. It tended to fix my attention on certain definite objects – it enabled me in many cases of doubt to correct my recollection by a reference to an exact record written at the time." This was not always quite true for the diary is sometimes written up many days later and there is some material which appears to have been re-written or recorded from other sources years later.

The diarist mentions two other useful reasons for his writing. In writing he was led to reflection and review, and in his review he hoped that he could feel satisfaction when it came to recording the next activities. Sadly volume I, the second large journal from 3 June 1823 to 31 December 1827 and the third large journal from 1 January 1828 are missing. The diarist explains that an extended journey to Scotland in April 1828 led him to start his second in smaller, pocket-sized notebooks.

The pocket-sized notebooks number one hundred and sixty-eight. They remain in the possession of the family and are also recorded on microfilm in the University Library of Newcastle-upon-Tyne as well as in the Northumberland County Archives. The diarist states in the first volume of this series that the substance of the first three volumes was printed in a small book for circulation amongst a few friends and the book was entitled *Reminiscences*. No copy of this has come to light. It may be that it was the *Reminiscences* rather than the first three large volumes to which B. W. Richardson had access when he wrote his biography of Thomas Sopwith (Longmans, Green & Co 1891). Richardson rightly pays tribute to the accuracy with which each entry is written "for cleanness of its style, and for the beauty of its penmanship."

The handwriting is superb copperplate in style. It continues throughout the one hundred and sixty-eight volumes with very little alteration and no sign of faltering. In a few diaries there are sketches. Some have lists of contents and some have indices. As a series of observations by a busy professional man they bear the stamp of a chronicle but when reflection is permitted, deeper insights are revealed. After writing 'THE END'. a final postscript is appended as follows:

"In 1822 I commenced a system of keeping a Journal or Account of my time which with some variations of Form has been steadily persevered in ever since. My first Journal was begun in 1821 but I did not preserve it. The 2nd and 3rd Vols were folio size but in 1828 I commenced Vol. I of the series corresponding in size with this volume & which series is 168 in number.

"A week has now passed over since I recorded on page 20 of this book the celebration of the 76th anniversary of my birth & having giving much consideration to the subject I have come to the conclusion not longer to continue it in this form and also to transfer my property therein to my dear Ursula without necessarily relinquishing my own possession. January 10 1878."

In this measured way he bade farewell with only slight inaccuracy. On 16 January 1879 he died.

Some Social Facts 1827

The careful habits of the diarist caused Sopwith to record various social facts in a summary to the memoranda for 1827.

In 1825 the Stamp Duty was nominally 4d, but a discount of twenty per cent was granted by Parliament against heavy excise duties, reducing the duty to 3¼d. The price of paper was seventy shillings per thousand for the large papers, or rather more than 4⅕d per sheet. The stamp and paper therefore cost rather more than 4d. He goes on to detail London newspaper editors' expenses both of paper and salaries paid out, noting that the cost of procuring reports of parliamentary proceedings for the daily papers was more than £3000 p.a. Whereas at one time two hundred and fifty impressions per hour were printed, steam power could increase that tenfold by 1827.

Statistics of population follow, especially comparing male and female, the fertility in marriage (four children was the average in the country, seven from two marriages in cities and large towns) while half of all children born in Great Britain died before the age of seventeen. He was able to refer to figures provided by the 1801 census and also gives details of death in cold weather as opposed to warm (in proportion seven to four) as well as the incidence of smallpox naturally caught and inoculated – the former being eight per one hundred, the latter one per three hundred. Religious fanaticism it is noted from some tables between 1772 and 1778 caused nearly one in eight cases of insanity.

B. W. Richardson's biography in which these statistics are reported speaks of the use of bells to signify special events, facts which were largely recorded in Brand's and Bourne's *Antiquities*. The Soul Bell could be rung for the funerals of the noted or wealthy. The great bell at St Nicholas' Church was also adapted to civil purposes, convening a guild-day or electing magistrates. A bell known as the Thief and Reever (robber) proclaimed two annual fairs. There was a reveille at 6 a.m. as well as the old curfew bell at 8 p.m. Sopwith liked the muffled bells on 30th January but did not realise their significance in marking the mourning for Charles I. These and many other useful facts were recorded along with a receipt for a scent-pot, "Calamus root 1½ ounces, Orris root 1 ounce, Musk 15 grains, add lavender flowers, damask rose leaves and bay salt, as much as you please."

Furniture

The joinery and cabinet-making enterprise which was established by Thomas Sopwith's grandfather in the 1760s flourished and continued as a retail outlet of high quality furniture until 1930. In that year it was bought by Chapman, now of Market Street. Although Thomas makes numerous references to items which he designed to be made in the family workshops, the premises which he himself relocated and designed in 1838, there are relatively few articles of furniture which can be specifically attributed to him. It is quite possible that early or mid-Victorian furniture made by the firm of T & J Sopwith remains to be discovered. The following list can safely be compiled either from written record or physical existence in 1991:

> Library book-cases at Wallington Hall, Northumberland c. 1853.
>
> Chairs and circular table at the Natural History Society room in Hancock Museum, Newcastle. c 1840.
>
> Chairs at Cragside, Rothbury, Northumberland.
>
> Monocleid desks. Various examples, including three at Sandon Hall, Staffordshire; a baroque version at the Great Exhibition at Crystal Palace, 1857; at Cragside, Rothbury.
>
> Sofa supplied to Ravensworth Castle.
>
> Travelling desk with detachable legs.

Thomas surrendered his interest in T & J Sopwith in November 1856 for £5,000, 'a gradual repayment of capital' to Thomas to the same amount and a lease of freehold and leasehold property for 21 years at an annual rental of £500.

A busy man's writing room

In 1838 at the end of a fulfilling year in which he had played host to friends in the British Association for the Advancement of Science, Sopwith paused to describe his library or writing room at 1 St. Mary's Terrace. It is a long description and unusually he repeats the page numbering before returning to other subjects. The detail is meticulous and has been abbreviated here. It reflects his pride and delight, as well as increasing sense of self-satisfaction, with the surroundings of a cultivated, practical man of science which he sought to portray. The account is contemporary and reveals the room "in which so many of my hours are passed with a degree of enjoyment which it would be difficult to surpass."

"First then on my left is a comfortable fire. . . the mantlepiece contains . . . the bowl of a Turkish pipe – A specimen of new concrete tiling – 2 polished specimens of Clifton Limestone – 3 patent inkstands . . . a wax taper – a porcelain bust of Wellington and a pistol . . . its barrel drilled out of a kitchen poker." There is a looking glass resting on the mantle and above it a water-colour of Greta Bridge near Keswick in a massive gilt frame. Other pictures are listed; a portrait of William Pitt, a view of Langley Castle, four of his own pen and ink drawings (three of which were engraved for Surtees' and Hodgson's *Histories of Durham and Northumberland*): there are local views, a portrait of him by Craft, T. M. Richardson's first original oil painting (a view of Cullercoats), J. W. Carmichael's first oil painting (a view of Jedburgh Abbey) and a portrait of John Hodgson of Hartburn.

"On each side of the Fire place are large closets . . . on the left

. . . my travelling portmanteau . . . plans and engravings . . . fossils from Cheltenham and four writing boxes or desks appropriated to different subjects." The other closet or cupboard has books, prints, minerals and two more desks or boxes. "The East side of the room has a window in the centre . . . on the left of it is the piano which formerly belonged to Miss Scott now my better half." He does practise on it occasionally – there is a better one in the drawing-room – and it has its use as "a sideboard and has now upon it a number of railway plans a tin chest containing Dean Forest papers . . . a book stand . . . and a splendid 20 inch globe . . . an object of great attraction to all my children except the youngest. Fronting the window is the sliding-table of my writing cabinet. Two reading stands contain several pamphlets . . . chiefly relating to Mines and Railways – My writing cabinet would require a long description . . . It contains an alphabet of pigeon-holes." This stands above the main writing area with papers on the Dean Forest Mining Commission, County Clare Mines, The BAAS, family notes, MSS including his *Essays on the Principles of Design*, catalogues of books, instruments and drawings. His travelling materials such as scales, drawing instruments, clinometer and pocket dials down to "red tape, lucifer matches, vestas and brass pins" are all listed. In the alphabet pigeon holes are accounts, valuations, current correspondence, letters, papers to be arranged, diaries. There is mention too of "the set of diaries for ten years past bound in green cloth and lettered." The 1840 example (see chapter 13 above) is almost certainly a later one of these. There is a very full catalogue of papers of recent importance and those currently concerning him. To the right of his monocleid, for so it is, are bookcases, "surmounted with plaster figures by Fiamingo" and some mineral specimens, some 76 books on professional subjects, including his own, mingle with his first folio journal, evidence and reports for railway bills and an arbitration. An iron safe painted to resemble mahogany contains large ledgers, indentures of his five clerks and various deeds. Another bookcase holds reference works including the *London Encyclopedia* (twenty-two volumes). A secretary or writing desk with drawers below the bookcase holds personal mementoes and minerals. A large bookcase nine foot long with seven rows of books and three cabinets beneath fills the final space on that side of the room. Here are some six hundred volumes "many of them richly bound" with large, unwieldy books in one of the three cabinets such as Lewis' topographical volumes and Stephenson on the Steam Engine. Highly prized on the shelves above are Surtees' *History of Durham*, three volumes folio at thirty guineas, a gift from Surtees himself. "The British Essayists are bound in green morocco in forty-five volumes . . . Swift's works in nineteen volumes are an amusing fund of instruction and entertainment. The works of Berkeley and Sterne are great favourites . . . Shakespeare Byron and Scott are not wanting." Some books will have been taken out "to supply the drawing room table": other treasures included eleven autograph letters of John Wesley in a fine album with portraits and cuttings. Along with all Sopwith's library in May 1879 this album was apparently sold for five shillings.

The final bookcase to be mentioned is "a very small one which forms a pedestal for a very beautiful model of St. Nicholas' steeple . . . this specimen of workmanship in tin is much admired . . . it contains a watch with a dial painted as a facsimile miniature of the church clock." A catalogue of an 1840 exhibition of Arts, Manufactures and Practical Science records that this model was on show along with T & J Sopwith's own furniture, designs and specimens of fine hardwoods but the maker's name is not recorded. The base of the model in the form of a turntable was "made of part of the very oak desk at which Stowell, Eldon and Collingwood pursued their studies under the less celebrated but equally excellent man, Hugh Moises."

Last of all is described the writing table in the centre of the room to complete a picture which, "if my children may take some interest in knowing the exact portraiture of my *time* and *place* and studies," would reflect his prosperous happiness at the time. In his second journal, now missing, he had described his room at Alston, but this had sad memories as he looked back to his first wife's briefest of motherhoods. Realising that he is digressing, Sopwith turns again to describe his table. It is part writing-desk of an entirely new construction at which he could stand to write. Two portfolios for carrying work to the office and a handsome rosewood stand with its contents are the final pieces observed. Amongst the contents is a Comic Almanac for 1839, a present from Mary Somerville of her *Connection of the Physical Sciences* and some guide books. Of Richardson's *Picture of Newcastle* we learn that it is "too prosy, sentimental and full of unimportant detail for my taste" and so, as he explains, "it was a dread of these qualities in a five shillings book that led me to write my brief 1s 6d guide."

Learned Societies

"A memorandum of the principal Institutions with which I am connected by membership" is listed in diary of journal number fifty-six in the year 1856. Ten double pages comment on the significance of each to him in perhaps an order of importance, followed by a neatly tabulated list in four classes.

At the head of the list is the Royal Society (FRS 1845) and he records "with some complacency" (pleasure) that the recommendations from personal knowledge were signed by eminent savants, a list mostly of geologists headed by Buckland, Fitton and Murchison, "the voluntary insertion of such names" giving as much satisfaction as anything in his life. He coupled this reflection with a glowing pride in his membership of the Athenaeum, for which his proposal paper was signed by similar and other luminaries in society. His proposer had been Sir Charles Lemon Bart M. P., the seconder the Dean of Westminster (Professor William Buckland): other names included Sir Henry de la Beche, Sir Charles Lyell, Decimus Burton and John Murray, the publisher. The Geological Society Club, an inner group of the Geological Society of London, of some thirty to thirty-six members, had long been a special pleasure since 1845: other geological names mentioned in this category are Sir Philip Egerton and Leonard Horner and membership included Robert Stephenson. The Geological Society (FGS 1835) was the arena into which he introduced thirteen friends, many from Newcastle including Robert Atkinson, William Cubitt, Joseph Dickinson and his brother-in-law Marcus Scott (described as of London). He had also been "mainly instrumental in the

19

I   General Science & Literature.

1. Royal Society.   F.R.S.,
7. Royal Institution.   M.R.I.,
10. British Association.   "
20. Lit. & Phil. Soc. N.Castle   "
" Cavendish Society.   "
" Percy Society.   "
" Shakespeare Society.   "
26. Surtees Society.   "

II   Geology, Mining, Engin.g & Usef.l Arts.

4. Geological Soc.y London. F.G.S.
5. Geological Soc.l France.   "
9. Palæontological Soc.?   "
18. Geolog. Soc. W.R.Yorks.   "
19. Geolog. Soc. Manchester.   "
21. Mining Inst. N.Castle   "
6. Institution Civil Eng.rs C.E.

III

11. Society of Arts.   "
  Geography, Meteorology & Nat.l Hist.
8. Geographical Soc.y "
13. Meteorological Soc. Lond. "
11. Meteorological Soc. Scott.? •
22. Nat.Hist. Soc. N.Castle. ——"
23. Tyneside Nat. Field Club — "

IV.   Statistics, Antiquities & Fine Arts.

12. Statistical Soc. Lond.   — •
15. Archæological Institute.   "
14. Archæological Association. "
25. Antiquar.n Soc. N.Castle. ——
21. North of Eng. Soc. Fine Arts "

Class			
I —	In London 5 —	Prov. 3 —	" 8.
II	Do — 4	Do. 4	8
III	Do . 2	Do 3	5
IV	Do 1	Do 4	5
	12	14	26

introduction of" George and Robert Stephenson, Rendel, Brunel and others. The Institution of Civil Engineers (member 1833) and The Geological Society of France (Life Fellow from 1844) were other marks of national and international distinction, Thomas Telford no less having seen "some geological and mechanical drawings . . . the latter was a machine for dressing lead ore." It was Telford who had proposed him as C. E. and in 1841 he had won the Telford silver medal for his geological models. In 1846 he was on the Council with such great names as I. K. Brunel, Joseph Locke and Robert Stephenson. To the Royal Institution, Michael Faraday had proposed Stephenson and Sopwith in June 1854 and the latter duly gave one of the expected Friday evening lectures. The Royal Geographical Society brought him access to a fine library and excellent maps while the Palaeontological Society's publications were a prized addition to his library. The British Association volumes included his outstanding part in establishing the Office of Mining Records. Copies of all the transactions of the Royal Society of Arts since 1783 sat on his shelves and of the Statistical Society's transactions, he refers to his friend Joseph Fletcher's *Moral Statistics*. The Meteorological Society of London was an opportunity for later honours, as President 1859-61, but he was very soon making regular observations at Allenheads and Bywell after taking up his post with the WB lead mines. He hoped to see the Meteorological Societies of Scotland and London join forces. His archaeological interests seem to have been edged to the periphery by 1845 but his initial membership of the Archaeological Association in 1844 was transferred to the Archaeological Institute of London from 1852. The more regional enthusiasms are reflected in geology, the promotion of fine arts, natural history, antiquarianism and of course in the Mining Institute of Newcastle. The Percy, Shakespeare and Cavendish Societies are described as Book clubs and finally he was proud to be elected an honorary member of the "Society for purchasing Books at Leadhills", one of the earliest libraries established by working men.

Appendix VI

A Family of Engineers

Thomas Sopwith was the founder of an engineering family of some note in the nineteenth and twentieth centuries. The surveying and engineering interests continue in current generations, but only the principal names are shown in the table with relevant qualifications:

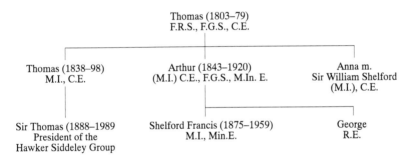

Thomas (1803–79)
F.R.S., F.G.S., C.E.

Thomas (1838–98)	Arthur (1843–1920)	Anna m.
M.I., C.E.	(M.I.) C.E., F.G.S., M.In. E.	Sir William Shelford
		(M.I.), C.E.

Sir Thomas (1888–1989	Shelford Francis (1875–1959)	George
President of the	M.I., Min.E.	R.E.
Hawker Siddeley Group		

Thomas (1838) had a wide experience of civil and mining engineering, notably at Linares, Spain, after apprenticeship at Sir William Armstrong's Elswick works on Tyneside. His son, Sir Thomas (1888), while not noted for his formal education, was a pioneer aviator who rose to control a major part of the aircraft industry.

Arthur (1843) not only had wide international mining experience following apprenticeship to a colliery viewer, but also pioneered the use of subterranean electricity and photography, continuing his father's interest in education and the practical application of geology, being President of the Institute of Mining Engineers and a member of coucil of the Imperial College of Science and Technology.

Anna's husband, William Shelford, and Thomas (1803) shared a mutual respect for each other's engineering work. Shelford Francis (1875) continued his father's direction of Cannock Chase collieries, patented the S.F. pit prop and served on the West Midlands Electricity Authority, extending the use of electricity in all parts of the collieries.

Notes

Chapter 1 Notes

1. T. S. Scrapbook
2. ibid
3. Freemen's Register 1755–1836
4. T. S. Scrapbook
5. Archaeologica Aeliana 30 107
6. Sopwith Memorandum of Views etc.
7. T. S. Scrapbook
8. Diary 1 p1, rewritten in 1855
9. Diary No. 26 p15
10. *Practical Observations on Surveying and Levelling* 1853
11. Richardson B. W. *Diary and Life of T. Sopwith* p10. Also note 8 above.
12. *Education: its present state and future advancement 1853*
13. Parson & White Gazetteer of the Counties of Durham and Northumberland 1827
14. Richardson p10
15. Diary 7 pp2–15
16. Richardson, quoting missing diary of April 20, 1828

Chapter 2 Notes

1. Richardson p20
2. Catalogue of Prints. There are several examples in the catalogue for sale in 1879
3. W. C. Trevelyan letters WCT 18
4. Sopwith Memorandum of Views etc.
5. See *A Historical and Descriptive Account of All Saint's Church*
6. Hodgson, Letter books
7. ibid
8. ibid
9. *An Account of the Mining District of Alston Moor, Weardale and Teesdale* by T. Sopwith 1833
10. Hodgson, *History of Northumberland* Part 2 Vol 2 introduction

11. Hodgson, letter to Sopwith 20 Nov 1830
12. Hodgson, journal
13. Hodgson Letter books 22 Oct 1832
14. ibid 20 Dec 1832
15. ibid 2 Feb 1833
16. ibid 16/17 July 1833, 23 Aug 1834,
17. Surtees to Sopwith, Dec 4 1832

Chapter 3 Notes

1. *A Treatise on Isometrical Drawing* 1834 and 1833 by T. Sopwith
2. Diary 34 p19, No 36 195–6
3. See p 48, Walter Scott and the wedding cake
4. Diary No 5 p17, quoted in Richardson
5. Diary lost, probably of 1825. See Richardson pp18, 19
6. Hodgson Letter books 12 Oct 1829
7. ibid 20 Dec 1832
8. ibid 11 Oct 1829
9. Belsay to Otterburn papers 1829–30
10. ibid 1829–30
11. The Otterburn Road by Wm. Lawson Archaeologica Aeliana series 4 vol 49
12. Belsay to Otterburn papers
13. Hodgson Letter book 11 Oct 1829
14. *Newcastle Courant*, quoted in Raine's *Memoir of Hodgson* p30
15. Local maps & plans vol 1 No 28, Lit & Phil Society, Newcastle

Chapter 4 Notes

1. *Surveying and Levelling* by T. Sopwith
2. ibid
3. *Account of an Improved Levelling Stave*
4. ibid
5. ibid
6. Diary August 1837
7. Diary
8. Miscellaneous Tracts. *The Monocleid.*

Chapter 5 Notes

1. Memorandum of Views
2. ibid
3. *Account of the Mining District of Alston Moor*, etc.
4. Memorandum of Views
5. T.S. Scrapbook
6. Memorandum of Views

7. Diaries 13, 28, 29, 31
8. Diary 1838
9. Diary 28, p422
10. Diary 28, p424
11. Diary 1, pp 14, 15
12. Raine Mss 117 1837
13. Raine Mss 117 1837
14. Raine Mss 117 1837
15. Diary 2 p12
16. T.S. Scrapbook

Chapter 6 Notes

1. *Reminiscences* Scrapbook
2. ibid
3. ibid
4. Diary No. 8 p2
5. Architectural Review May 1946
6. Diary 9 pp 6,7
7. Diary 6 pp 3,9
8. *Reminiscences* Scrapbook

Chapter 7 Notes

1. Diary 1 pp 1,2
2. Diary 1 p13
3. Diary 1 p20
4. Diary 1 p56
5. Diary 3 pp 3–12
6. Diary 8 pp 120–122
7. Diary 4 p41
8. Diary 6 p77
9. Richardson p87
10. Diary 5 pp17–19
11. Diary 38 pp38–9

Chapter 8 Notes

1. Diary 3 p11
2. Diary 3 p14
3. Diary 3 p19
4. Diary 3 p34

Chapter 9 Notes

1. Diary 3 p49
2. Diary 3 p52
3. Diary 3 p54
4. Diary 3 p56
5. Local Tracts L042, Newcastle City Lib.
6. Diary 7 p90

Chapter 10 Notes

1. Richardson p47
2. *Reminiscences* Scrapbook
3. Hedley's humour is expressed in a letter to Hodgson. If only he (Hedley) could find a living as valuable as Mitford, "and passing rich should I think myself with its ninety pounds a year . . . but I am quite as likely to get Sopwith's Bishopric!". Did Hedley mean that Sopwith's flattery indicated that Hedley should be a bishop? See also Diary 10 pp74–6. Soc. of Antiqs., Newcastle. Hodgson's letter books.
4. Diary 5 1834 pp3–5, See p19
5. Diary 5 1834 p60
6. *Reminiscences* Scrapbook
7. Diary 5 p49
8. Diary 3 p35
9. Diary 5 p16a July 1833
10. Diary 7 p31
11. Diary 8 p30,1
12. Diary 9 p28
13. Diary 32 p124
14. Diary 34 pp 10, 11
15. Diary 34 p38
16. Diary 35 p130
17. Diary 14 pp68, 9
18. Diary 32 p107
19. Diary 2 p15
20. Diary 2 p18
21. Diary 3 p22
22. Diary 27 pp 341,2
23. Diary 3 p14, 15
24. Diary 6 p92
25. Diary 17 p112
26. Diary 20 p314
27. Diary 21 p42
28. Diary 30 p2

29. Diary 32 p80

Chapter 11 Notes

1. Public Record Office F17/426
2. P.R.O. F16/34
3. P.R.O. F20/6
4. Diary 4 p76
5. Diary 4 p83
6. Diary 4 p85
7. Diary 4 p79
8. P.R.O. F17/6
9. P.R.O. F17/32
10. P.R.O. F17/18(3)
11. Diary 6 p61
12. Diary 7 p54
13. W. C. Trevelyan papers WCT216
14. Diary 7 p58
15. Diary 11 p77
16. P.R.O. F20/6
17. P.R.O. F20/6
18. Diary 11 p79
19. Diary 11 p79
20. Diary 11 p111
21. Diary 12 p37
22. P.R.O. F20/6
23. Diary 19 p268
24. Diary 23 p39
25. Diary 19 p257

Chapter 12 Notes

1. Marie Boase Hall, *All Scientists Now* CUP 1984
2. J. Morrell & A. Thackray, *Gentlemen of Science* CUP 1981
3. Diary 2 p73, 3 p71, 7 p90
4. Diary 7 p56–9
5. Diary 7 p59
6. Diary 7 p73
7. Diary 7 p76
8. Diary 17 pp160–3
9. Diary 22 p39
10. Diary 22 p40
11. Diary 24 pp74–5
12. Diary 26 pp247–8
13. Diary 26 p242

14. Diary 26 p253
15. Diary 26 p58
16. Diary 27 p331
17. Diary 29 p464–5
18. Diary 32 p116 & No 33 p297
19. Morrell & Thackray op cit p260
20. Quoted in M & T pp260–1
21. Morrell & Thackray p265
22. Diary 10 p95
23. Diary 11 p46
24. Diary 11 p61
25. Richardson p222
26. Diary No. 41 p87

Chapter 13 Notes

1. Diary 25 pp 144–5
2. Diary 23 p11
3. Diary 23 p16
4. Diary 23 p29
5. Diary 23 p39
6. Diary 23 p59
7. Diary 24 p125
8. Diary 25 p172,2
9. Diary 26 p217
10. 1840 Notebook

Chapter 14 Notes

1. Diary 1 p.i
2. *Account of the Mining District of Alston Moor*, etc. p.86
3. Diary 1 p63
4. Letters for August and September WCT 216
5. Geological sections of Holyfield etc. Newcastle Town Lib. Misc. Tracts L622.34
6. Adapted from S. Turner and W. R, Dearman, *Thomas Sopwith's geological models* 1982, Yorks. Geological Soc.
7. *Isometric Drawing* by T. Sopwith 2nd edition 1838
8. Diary 2 p63
9. Diary 3 p62
10. Diary 7 p90
11. Diary 5 p23
12. Diary 8 p118
13. Diary 11 p64

14. Diary 31 p102
15. Diary 25 p147
16. *Description of Sopwith's Geological Models* 1875 p74
17. W.R. Dearman and S. Turner, *Models illustrating John Farey's figures of stratified masses* (1983), Proceedings of Geological Association 94(2) pp97–104
18. Ibid p104
19. Diary 24 p116
20. Ibid p120
21. W.R. Dearman and S. Turner, Geological Curators Group 2 pp467–95
22. Diary 27 p351–2
23. Diary 39 p32
24. *The National Importance of Preserving Mining Records*, by T. Sopwith

Chapter 15 Notes

1. Diary 35 p94
2. Diary 35 p180
3. Diary 35 p142
4. Diary 36 p158
5. Diary 36 p160
6. Diary 38 p23
7. Diary 38 unnumbered page. Entry for September 7th
8. Diary 38 p80
9. Diary 39 p52
10. Diary 39 p14
11. Diary 39 p63

Chapter 16 Notes

1. Diary 41 p78
2. Diary 41 pp78–9
3. Diary 41 p96
4. Diary 41 p99
5. Diary 41 p99
6. Diary 41 p136
7. Diary 42 p11

Index

This index gives references to the principal subjects and includes several names not readily identifiable but which may enable those with specialized knowledge to supply a more certain identity. First names, titles and occupations are recorded as Thomas Sopwith knew them, with some adaptation from the *Dictionary of National Biography*.